History and Methods of Physiological Psychology

A BRIEF OVERVIEW

SHELDON J. LACHMAN

Wayne State University

THE HAMILTON PRESS

Detroit, Michigan

THE HAMILTON PRESS
Detroit, Michigan

CONTENTS

PART I

HISTORY OF PHYSIOLOGICAL PSYCHOLOGY

PART II

METHODS OF PHYSIOLOGICAL PSYCHOLOGY

PREFACE

The intent of this brief book is to present a concise survey of the history and methods of physiological psychology.

Essentially, it is a slightly edited transcript of lectures presented in 1961 and 1962 to first year psychology graduate students at Wayne State University in a required General Psychology Proseminar. Since inquiry disclosed no brief and comprehensive presentation of the history or of the methods of physiological psychology and since the time allotment for the physiological psychology material was so abbreviated, it was deemed appropriate to reduce the lectures on history and methods to written form with the purpose of preserving more class time for discussing other topics—especially the psychophysiology of learning.

The history of the field as herein outlined is basically a factual account and has been organized with an emphasis on chronological succession. Ordinarily, histories in a field of science are written with emphasis on the development of ideas, methods, and other contributions. A principal advantage of a chronological technique is its economy. When history is presented in terms of the development of distinct ideas and methods, an outstanding contributor may be mentioned in 5 or 10 or even 20 different places; it seemed to the author less confusing and less redundant to present contributions of a particular individual only once, or certainly as few times as necessary; admittedly in so doing, for the advantages gained, certain other desirable features have probably been lost. In considering the history of physiological psychology, an attempt has been made to assess what to the author appear to be meaningful trends of the last 15 or 20 years.

In the methods section attention has been paid to both clinical and experimental methods. The special advantages and limitations of each of these broad categories of method have been evaluated.

The author is grateful to several of his colleagues at Wayne

1

State University, in connection with the development of the manuscript, especially to Wilson McTeer of the Psychology Department for reviewing and criticizing the history section and to Alfred Stern of Monteith College for considering and evaluating both sections. Their suggestions have resulted in improvement of the presentation.

SHELDON J. LACHMAN

Wayne State University
Detroit, Michigan
March 29, 1963

I

History of Physiological Psychology

I. The Province of Physiological Psychology

Physiological psychology is the scientific study of the relationships between the behavior of organisms and the biological nature of organisms.

The basic objective of physiological psychology is to determine the biological correlates of behavior—to ascertain the anatomical and physiological foundations of behavior.

In general psychology, the S-O-R formula, in which S represents stimulus, O the organism, and R response, is often cited. Likewise, there is an extensively developed S-R psychology which is concerned with relationships between S and R, ignoring very much the intervening O. Some psychologists hold that the nature of the O is strictly a biological problem and need not concern the psychologist—that the psychologist need concern himself only with behavior and that the biological nature of the O can be conveniently ignored. Furthermore, on the basis of empirical observation of S and R relationships, relatively accurate predictions of response have been made from knowledge of the stimulus alone, without detailed information about the biological nature of the organism. Nevertheless, other knowledge areas are neglected by this procedure.

Despite progress in ascertaining many relationships between S and R, the adequacy of an S-R psychology is questioned. There are intraorganismic or intervening variables which influence behavior. With an understanding of these variables, accuracy in the prediction of behavior is improved. The organism is a natural object and can be studied. In other words, with a knowledge of the biological nature of the organism, behavior can be better understood and predicted. Physiological psychology is much concerned with the intraorganismic changes which intervene between stimulus and response.

It is possible to deal only with the stimuli or inputs and

with responses or outputs and to regard the organism as a black box, the interior of which is to be ignored. But the nature, that is, the structures and functions, of that black box interior limit and otherwise much influence the quality of output with respect to a given input. Let us consider two black boxes which appear to be identical. Each has two input areas A and B and an output area C. Appropriate quantities of input in A and B set into operation the mechanism of the box and produce outputs at C. If in box I, given quantities of tobacco are put into A and thin paper is put into B, rolled cigarettes are obtained in a short time at C. If in box II, black ink is put into A and heavy paper into B, printed sheets of paper are released at C. However, if the contributions for the two boxes are reversed, then for box I a chaotic mixture of ink and paper are obtained at C and for box II an unorganized mixture of tobacco and mangled paper is discharged at C. *To understand the relationships of the inputs to the outputs, it is necessary to have knowledge of the mechanism within the black box.* It is possible to hypothesize and make inferences about the nature of the internal mechanisms of the black box through an analysis of relationships between energies applied and reactions evoked. But why speculate, when knowledge may be obtained by more direct observation?

Suppose that the black box appears, on the basis of external inspection, to be in a satisfactory state and that external conditions are appropriate, but that now responses are very unusual, that is, quite different than they were previously—how are these to be understood? Again the suggestion is made that *understanding is facilitated by directly examining the mechanism.* Systematic observation of the structural nature of the organismic mechanism and its functioning in relationship to organismic behavior with the goal of improved understanding is the province of physiological psychology.

II. Pseudopsychophysiologies

Pseudopsychophysiologies are doctrines which purport to indicate relationships between the biological nature of the organism and its behavior, but which are unfounded, that is, they are not based on careful and systematic observation. One such field is physiognomy; another is phrenology. Both are in disrepute and neither is given serious consideration within

4

science at the present time, although since they have had some influence on the development of physiological psychology in the past, they are of historical interest.

Physiognomy is the doctrine which holds that physical characteristics of the face and body are indicative of psychological traits, i.e., traits of character, temperament, intellect, or personality. Table 1 summarizes a few physiognomic notions which to some extent persist—at least in colloquial speech.

Table 1. UNSUPPORTED PHYSIOGNOMIC NOTIONS

Physical Characteristic	Psychological Characteristic
Red hair	Emotional instability
High forehead	High intelligence
Protruding chin	Aggressiveness
Slender fingers	Artistic talent
Chest hair	Masculinity
Stout—Thin	Jolliness—Melancholia
Large ears	Generosity
Full lips	Sensuousness
Thick short neck	Stubbornness
Dark skin	Rhythmic sense

This kind of direct, simple one-to-one relationship between physical and psychological characteristics proposed in physiognomic propositions is not supported by evidence and there is much evidence opposed.

Phrenology is a doctrine again unsupported by evidence, according to which from an analysis of protrusions and depressions in the skull, various traits of character, temperament, personality and intellect are ascertained. For phrenology, also, there is much opposed evidence.

III. Relationships Between the Mental and the Material: The Mind-Body Problem

Throughout the centuries many suggestions have been made regarding the foundations of behavior. The concept of animism is believed to be among the oldest. Primitive people today, and perhaps also our primitive ancestors attempted to account for phenomena, otherwise mysterious and inexplicable to them, such as thunder, lightning, windstorms, cloud movement, earthquakes, and the like, by specifying a hidden man or demon in the thunder, lightning, wind, cloud, and earth. This doctrine was extended to account for behavior in fellow men which was not readily understood, by proposing hidden spirits or demons or men within the man who behaved in an unusual way.

More sophisticated conceptions of the relationships of the psychological to the physical are considered as an aspect of philosophical dualism called the mind-body problem. In essence, the problem might be briefly stated this way: There is a mind or "psychological entity" and there is a body or physical organism. In what way are they alike and in what way are they different? What are the relationships between the two? Throughout history several attempts have been made to solve the problem. In general, there has been fair agreement on what is meant by body, but concepts of mind and conceptions regarding the relationships between mind and body have been diverse.

Among the earliest recorded suggestions is the double-aspect theory of ARISTOTLE (384-322 BC). According to it, mind and body are two aspects of the same thing; they cannot be separated. If the body is substance, then the mind is the form of that substance. Aristotle conceived of mind as a function of the body. Since the body has several classes of function, Aristotle proposed several classes of mind. The vegetative mind was characteristic of plants and it included all functions having to do with internally regulated processes which permitted the plant to maintain itself. Animals (which also had plant minds) had animal minds and these were characterized by properties of sensitivity and responsiveness, ways in which animals were distinct from plants. The human mind, sometimes called the rational mind, possessed functions of reasoning. Humans, of course, also possessed the animal mind and the vegetative mind.

RENÉ DESCARTES (1596-1650) proposed a perspective now known as psychophysical interactionism. Mind and body, according to this viewpoint, were distinct. The body was material and occupied space. Mind was immaterial and occupied no space. Descartes also had a mechanistic notion of living organisms; animals behaved like machines and were to be understood in terms of the same physical principles which permitted understanding of machines. This mechanistic notion was somewhat modified in the case of man, however: Man had a mind or soul conceived as a free agent which transcended mere physical laws and the mind could from time to time take over

6

operation of the body. Descartes conceived of the interaction between mind and body as occurring at the pineal gland— one of the few unpaired structures within the brain which is located deep within the midline region.

BARUCH SPINOZA (1632-1677) had a pantheistic viewpoint —a viewpoint holding that the supreme deity and the universe were the same; he further held that this universe is multiphasic or multidimensional and that man can know but two of these aspects, the physical and the mental. He held that there were parallels between the mental world or world of ideas and the physical world. Examples from geometry were used by Spinoza to illustrate his parallelism. Measurements inferred strictly on the basis of geometric ideas are paralleled in the physical world when actual measurements are made.

Another notion of psychophysical parallelism was suggested by GOTTFRIED WILHELM LEIBNITZ (1646-1716). He conceived of mind and body as two separate but parallel streams of activity. They did not influence each other and were not causally related but the same conditions guided the operation of each in parallel ways. One might think of two pools of water, or two clocks, labelling one of each pair mind and the other body. Under a given set of circumstances what occurs in one of those "systems" would also occur in the other under the same set of circumstances. Two parallel clocks, both operating "perfectly" and both continuously reporting the same identical times, but neither causing nor influencing the operation of the other, would provide in their parallel but independent operations an illustration of Leibnitz's conception of parallel independence of mind and body.

The identity concept, one aspect of a monistic philosophy, has been inferred by JOHN B. WATSON (1878-1958) and is supported by many of his behavioristic successors. According to it, mind and body are inseparable and identical. In this case, mind refers to behavior. As long as an organism lives it behaves; the behavior cannot exist independently of the organism doing the behaving. If one studies a living organism one observes behavior, and the observed behavior which the psychologist studies is not independent of the living organism. There is no question but that the last viewpoint has been of great value in the recent development of psychology.

In reconsidering the development of ideas concerning the

mind, it is to be noted that mind has had a variety of meanings including external force, soul, function of the organism, memory, consciousness, ideation, the brain, and behavior. In the course of the changes from the older philosophies to the viewpoints of modern psychology, the term mind which began with vague and mystical connotations and later had religious implications, has become progressively more definite and specifiable in terms of palpable overt phenomena.

IV. Ideas in the Historical Background of Physiological Psychology to the Nineteenth Century

The background of ideas in physiological psychology is long and complex. In a brief space, only a relatively few of them can be considered. Among the ancients, several of the great thinkers including Pythagoras, Plato, and Galen believed that the brain was the seat of the mind. Greek science reached a pinnacle in about the 3rd and 4th centuries B.C. after which a decline occurred and it was about 2000 years later in the 16th century world of Copernicus and Galileo that a revival began.

Beginning with the 18th century, several French thinkers proposed mechanistic notions of man. These philosophers were much influenced by Descartes and also by JOHN LOCKE (1632-1704), an Englishman who encouraged the belief that there are no innate ideas and that all knowledge of the world must be derived through the senses; for Locke, the mind was a blank slate or *tabula rasa* upon which the experiences of life are written. Mind was redefined by Locke so that it could be thought of as the sum of the sense experiences of the individual and no longer needed to be confused with the religious soul.

A. The French Mechanists

Representative of the French mechanists were Condillac, la Mettrie and Cabanis.

1. ÉTIENNE BONNOT DE CONDILLAC (1715-1780) in elaborating Locke's *tabula rasa* idea suggested that man's mental life can be understood by beginning with experience: Imagine a statue endowed with but a single sense, for example, the odor sense. Suppose (1) the odor of a presented rose is detected; (2) then later an odor of tar is presented and detected; and

8

(3) still later the rose is presented again. Apparently the odor of the (1) rose and (2) tar are *detected* and *discriminated* from each other. They can be *compared* with each other with regard to quality and intensity. When the (3) rose is presented a second time there is the opportunity for *recognition memory*. In this proposed prototype of man, Condillac attempted to demonstrate such psychological functions as discrimination, comparison, recognition memory, value, judgment, and imagination as well as others; having provided a basic rationale for such attributes, Condillac proceeded to expand and complicate the model by adding other senses.

2. JULIEN OFFROY DE LA METTRIE (1709-1751) indicated that thought is nothing but the mechanical action of the brain and the nervous system. He did not distinguish between thought and soul. For La Mettrie, the soul was as mortal as the brain. He regarded man as a machine and in fact wrote a book titled "L'Homme Machine." La Mettrie taught that animals, including man, were automata.

3. PIERRE JEAN GEORGES CABANIS (1757-1808), was a professor at the University of Paris and became physician to Mirabeau at the time of the French Revolution. It was observed then that there were bodily movements of persons who had been guillotined; in 1795 Cabanis was officially asked to determine whether such victims of the guillotine were conscious after decapitation. He decided that the postdecapitation reactions were mechanical and on an unconscious level. Cabanis suggested three levels or states of activity: (a) Unconscious states which were identified by simple automatic reactions, presumably involving integration only at the level of the spinal cord. (b) Semiconscious states which depended somewhat on brain action. (c) Conscious states which were dependent exclusively on brain action.

B. Other Pre-Nineteenth Century Contributors

Among the other pre-nineteenth contributors deserving mention are Von Haller and Gall and his associates.

One aspect of a modified doctrine of irritability proposed by ALBRECHT VON HALLER (1708-1777) suggested that regardless of how excitation was initiated, the energy for muscular contraction was supplied from within the muscle. In certain respects this concept was a forerunner of the doctrine of specific nerve energies.

FRANZ JOSEPH GALL (1758-1828) is regarded as the formulator of phrenology. He was an anatomist specializing in the head and brain and he began his lectures on phrenology in Vienna in 1796. Basically, phrenology is the doctrine which proposed that psychological traits (or faculties) of personality, intellect, temperament, and character are ascertainable from analysis of the protrusions and depressions in the skull.

According to this doctrine, the faculties were located in particular regions of the brain; enlargements or depressions in the brain in particular areas meant a greater than normal or less than normal quantity of the faculty; it was further assumed that the external contour of the skull accurately reflected the external contour of the brain.

Gall's doctrine was based on quite casual and unsystematic investigation. He observed prominences in a particular region of the skull in some pickpockets and suggested that the faculty of personal acquisitiveness was located in that region. A woman he knew whose outstanding trait was sociability had an enlargement at the side of her head; on that basis he localized the "sociability" (adhesiveness) bump in that region. Gall had casts made of the heads of friends and of persons whose prominent psychological characteristics were well known and he studied these.

In 1800 he was joined by JOHANN C. SPURZHEIM (1776-1832) who became at first Gall's disciple and later an associate. In 1807 Gall settled in Paris and with Spurzheim elaborated and extended Gall's basic doctrine and wrote a series of books on it. He suggested some 37 "powers" of mind; the brain was regarded as the organ of mind and the 37 powers of mind corresponded to 37 more specific brain regions. Phrenology had great popular appeal and thrived during the 19th century. However, in general, it was held in low regard by men of science; its methodology was questioned and the propagandizing efforts of some of its supporters was held in poor taste; in addition, there was insufficient supporting evidence. Attacks on phrenology came from many directions, three of which may be specified:

(1) Attacks by the intellectually skeptical: They pointed to a lack of sufficient evidence concerning relationships between so-called faculties and skull prominences.

(2) Attacks by physiologists: The physiologists presented evidence controverting the relationships proposed between external contour of the skull and function of particular brain regions.

(3) Attacks by philosophers: They objected to an analysis of "mind" into faculties with spatially distinct organs; that idea violated the principle of unity of mind—a strongly entrenched belief.

The evidence against phrenology came from many directions: (1) One implication of the doctrine was that the greater the size of the brain the greater the intelligence. However, there were many persons with unusually large skulls (and brains) who were very severely retarded mentally and other persons with small skulls (and brains) who were clearly of exceptionally superior intellectual competence. (2) The relationships between skull shape and brain contour were often revealed on postmortem examination to be quite different. (3) Actual brain functions as empirically ascertained by physiologists were quite different from those proposed by the phrenologists.

Although the basic view was erroneous and has not survived, nevertheless the theory was of some value in further scientific thought:

(1) It emphasized the brain as the "organ of mind" and this belief oriented science in the direction which led to the development of a scientific physiological psychology. Mind was not a matter for metaphysical speculation only. This modification in thinking facilitated receptivity to empirical evidence. Mental functions and the body were no longer regarded as separate and distinct but as inextricably related. The concept provided an intellectual framework for further theorizing and research.

(2) It suggested a localization of function in the brain. This was an overt and useful hypothesis for investigation.

(3) It rendered a service by calling attention to the phenomena of individual differences as opposed to the notion of a generalized mind.

(4) It encouraged an empirical method. Gall himself encouraged objectivity and inductive reasoning.

On behalf of Gall it should be said that he was a brilliant neuroanatomist and made many contributions to the field of neuroanatomy; it is unfortunate that he is so often remembered only in terms of his theory of phrenology.

V. Contributions to Physiological Psychology in the Nineteenth Century

A. Major Contributions in the Early Nineteenth Century

Foundations for a sound psychophysiology began in the nineteenth century. In the early nineteenth century major contributions were made by Bell, Magendie, Flourens, and Hall.

SIR CHARLES BELL (1774-1842), an English physiologist, anatomist, surgeon, and lecturer discovered the law of the roots and published his findings in 1811. In simplest form the law of the roots specifies that the dorsal roots of the spinal cord are afferent or sensory in function and the ventral roots are efferent or motor in function; in other words, dorsal and ventral roots of spinal nerves are structurally and functionally discrete. Bell also suggested that separate regions of the spinal cord and brain might serve separate sensory (and motor) functions and in this he anticipated the doctrine of specific nerve energies. His findings also implied the principle of unidirectional conduction, namely, that conduction normally occurs in one direction—not both. Until the time of Bell it was generally assumed that nerves conducted in both directions and that all nerves had both afferent and efferent functions.

FRANÇOIS MAGENDIE (1783-1855) a contemporary of Bell who was the outstanding physiologist of France, apparently independently formulated in 1822, a similar principle concerning the functions of spinal nerve roots. He provided research evidence with several careful experiments which firmly established functions of spinal nerve roots and, for that reason, the law of the roots is sometimes called the Bell-Magendie Law.

M. J. PIERRE FLOURENS (1794-1867) opposed the views of Gall. He argued that while there were specific functions narrowly localized in the brain, there were also general functions which depended on larger portions of the brain. Flourens insisted on precise methods of direct observation; he skillfully used the method of extirpation of parts in a systematic attempt to determine functions of different regions of the brain. He suggested distinct functions for various parts of the brain. For

12

the cerebral lobes these were willing, judging, remembering, seeing, hearing, and several more; for the cerebellum, the co-ordination of locomotor movements; for the medulla oblongata, vital activities; for the corpora quadrigemina, vision; for the spinal cord, conduction of excitation, and so on. His analysis pointed to a doctrine of levels of function but he emphasized that the nervous system was a "unitary system" and many of his conclusions about functions, though gross, are today still regarded for the most part as fairly accurate.

MARSHALL HALL (1790-1857), a Scottish physician working in London, insisted on a distinction between voluntary and involuntary action. Hall held that reflexes depend only on the spinal cord, never on the brain, and are always unconscious. He discovered that a decapitated newt responds to stimulation of the skin and studied the reflex activities of snakes after severing the spinal cord between the second and third vertebrae.

B. Major Contributions During the Middle Part of the Nineteenth Century

Major contributions during the middle part of the nineteenth century were made by Mueller, Bernard, du Bois-Reymond, Helmholtz, Darwin, and Broca.

JOHANNES P. MUELLER (1801-1858) was a prominent German physiologist whose great work was *Handbuch der Physiologie des Menschen* (1833-1840) which consisted of eight books and was an exhaustive summary of the physiology of that time. It contained many original observations and speculations and his contributions therein on the physiology of the nerves and the senses is of particular relevance to psychology. In it he formulated the doctrine of specific nerve energies, according to which the quality of sensation following sensory stimulation depends on the sensory system activated and not on the nature of the stimulus. In other words, if the visual system were activated by pressure applied to it or by electric shock, visual sensations would occur; if the auditory system were aroused by electric shock or by pressure, auditory sensations occur. Although the doctrine can now be subject to much criticism, it was an important and exciting formulation.

Du Bois-Reymond and Helmholtz who had been two of Mueller's students, later themselves made substantial contributions to those areas of mutual interest to psychologists and physiologists.

The researches of EMIL DU BOIS-REYMOND (1818-1896) served to remove the nervous impulse from the realm of the mystical, with its concern about animal spirits and the pneumatics of the soul, into the materialistic realm of science. One comment of du Bois-Reymond to the effect that if it were possible to cross-connect the auditory and optic nerves we ought to see sounds with our ears and hear light with our eyes, is a way of clarifying the intent of the doctrine of specific nerve energies. He is saying that under such circumstances we should see thunder and hear lightning. He formulated a principle known since as the du Bois-Reymond Law which states that it is the variation or change in a stimulating agent within a short temporal interval which serves adequately to stimulate, not the absolute value of the stimuluus.

Another of Mueller's students, HERMAN LUDWIG FERDINAND VON HELMHOLTZ (1821-1894) made substantial contributions to physics and physiology as well as to psychology. He prepared distinguished treatises in physiological optics and physiological acoustics and did outstanding work in the field of hydrodynamics, electrodynamics, meteorological physics, and on the conservation of energy. Mueller had earlier taught that the speed of the nerve impulse was virtually instantaneous or at least on the order of light velocity. In fact, at one point he suggested a speed of 11 million miles per second—about 60 times the velocity of light and he wrote that "We shall never attain the power of measuring the velocity of nervous action. . . ." However, du Bois-Reymond suggested to Helmholtz that the speed of the nerve impulse was finite and measurable. In 1850, Helmholtz measured the rate of transmission of the nervous impulse—a most spectacular discovery. He found the impulse velocity to be relatively slow—in the frog about 30 meters per second and in man between 50 and 100 meters per second.

Helmholtz developed an ingeniously simple but convincing technique for measuring nerve impulse velocity. He excited through independent electrical stimulation at two points, the sciatic nerve attached to the gastrocnemius muscle of the frog: (a) One stimulated point, *a* was a considerable distance from the muscle; (b) the other stimulated point, *b,* was much nearer the muscle. Helmholtz measured the length of time between stimulation at point *a* and contraction of the muscle; he also measured the length of time between stimulation at point *b* and contraction of the muscle. The difference in time required to produce muscle contraction, inferred Helmholtz, must be due to differences in the location of the two points of stimulation, one being much farther away from the muscle than the other. Hence, this time, the *difference time,* is the time required for the impulse to travel between point *a* and point *b*. By measuring the distance between points *a* and *b,* and dividing the *time* inferred to be required for the impulse to travel this distance (the difference time) into this *distance,* it is possible to ascertain the velocity of conduction per unit of time. It is difficult to overestimate the importance of this contribution. There was, of course, much resistance to acceptance of the idea that nervous conduction was measurable and that it was so slow. The bases for "mind" and for thinking with this discovery were not now forever unknowable. Since conduction was not instantaneous, neither was thought. Both were actually detectable and finite. Helmholtz's finding in this regard provided something of a basis for early psychological measurement; it served also effectively to tie the behavior of the organism to the physiological functioning of the organism.

Helmholtz also proposed comprehensive sensory theories of vision (1856) and audition (1863) which have stood the test of time and each, in modified form, remains prominent in contemporary sensory psychophysiology. His three factor theory of color vision proposed three different kinds of photoreceptor in the retina, one maximally sensitive to waves from the red part of the spectrum, another maximally sensitive to green, and a third most sensitive to blue. Patterns of color experience, then, are dependent upon the relative strengths with which the three types of photoreceptor are stimulated by objective light. Helmholtz's concept seemed to fit in well with Mueller's doctrine, and, in fact, is an extension of it. While Mueller emphasized discrete sensory modalities, and indicated that each sensory nerve stimulated gives rise to but one type of sensory process, Helmholtz further suggested that there may be several different kinds of sensory nerve fiber for a particular sensory modality (and presumably several different processes) and in this way endeavored to account for different qualities

15

or kinds of experience within a given sensory modality, e.g., for example, in vision more specific qualities might be green, red, and blue.

Helmholtz's theory of audition is sometimes called a place-resonance theory. He likened the auditory mechanism to a piano keyboard or harp. Each discriminable pitch is considered a function of selective activation of different parts of some structure in the cochlea, probably the basilar membrane. Individual fibers in the basilar membrane are excited by particular frequencies; this is a sympathetic resonating action. Again, the theory is consistent with Mueller's doctrine.

CHARLES ROBERT DARWIN (1809-1882) is generally credited with formulating the basic ideas of current doctrines of biological evolution; the general concept of evolution was not new, but Darwin, in *The Origin of Species* (1859), presented a great mass of supporting evidence in a coherent way. The central idea of the doctrine is that more complex organisms developed from the simpler by infinitesimal gradations over the course of eons of time. Essentially, the doctrine maintains that: (a) Organisms struggle for survival. (b) Individual members of a species are not identical but display some variation. (c) The environment, animate and inanimate, plays a role in selecting particular organisms for survival from the variations, i.e., certain organisms are eliminated and others permitted to survive, reach maturity and perpetuate the species by begetting offspring. (d) Organisms displaying characteristics which are best adapted to the environment survive while those with less appropriate characteristics fail to survive, i.e., protective coloration, claws permitting rapid tree climbing or effective attacking, animals capable of swimming, or animals with an auditory mechanism which is highly sensitive and permits ready detection of prey, and the like are characteristics which may permit adaptation and survival. (e) Through a succession of changes, perhaps in part a function of interaction with different environments which select out different characteristics, two distinct species may evolve from a common ancestor.

On the whole, Darwin proposed an extensive and plausible theory of an evolutionary origin of species; the theory stresses continuity of species. According to it, all structures have functions which contribute to survival. The behaviors of organisms (which of course depend on and are limited by biological struc-

16

ture) have a major role in survival; this idea served to bind psychology closer to biology. Mental processes were often stated in terms of function and in terms of adjusting to the world, and the school of functionalism in psychology was an intellectual descendant of this evolutionary biology.

In his work, *The Descent of Man* (1871), Darwin emphasized the similarity between human reasoning and certain psychological processes in other "highly developed" organisms. In his *Expression of Emotion in Man and Animals* (1872), he suggested an evolutionary interpretation of characteristic facial and postural changes during strong emotion. The evolutionary concept laid the groundwork for a comparative viewpoint in psychology; it also provided a bridge between human and other organisms, both biologically and psychologically.

CLAUDE BERNARD (1813-1878) worked as an assistant to Magendie for many years. His major research work involved a series of experiments on the glycogenic function of the liver; he also demonstrated the significance of pancreatic secretion in the digestive process. These investigations had relevance for the chemistry of organisms and the nature of the internal environment of the living organism. Although he did little work directly on endocrines, his research on liver functions and his stress on the "milieue interne" have led to Bernard's being called the "Father of Endocrinology." His concepts antedated later proposals of homeostasis and also came later to have special meaning for a psychology of emotion.

In 1861 PAUL BROCA (1824-1880) announced the localization of a center for speech at the base of the third frontal convolution of the left cerebral hemisphere. Early that year a patient with a gangrenous infection was cared for by Broca. This man had been at the Bicetre, a mental hospital, for about 30 years. He communicated with others effectively by gestures and his sole deficit seemed to be that he could not speak. Broca determined that there was no paralysis of peripheral speech mechanisms. The patient passed away within a short time after Broca examined him and Broca's autopsy disclosed a lesion in the third frontal convolution of the left cerebral hemisphere. On the basis of this immediate finding plus his knowledge of other supporting cases, Broca hazarded the suggestion that the third frontal convolution of the left cerebral hemisphere contained the center for spoken language. Broca further suggested that his discovery provided support for the general principle of localization of function; Gall and Spurzheim had been criticized earlier in the century for strenuously advocating a localization of function doctrine.

C. Major Contributions During the Later Part of the Nineteenth Century

During the last third of the nineteenth century, some of the major contributions to the developing field of psychophysiology were made by Fritsch and Hitzig and by Wundt in Germany and by Jackson and Morgan in England.

GUSTAVE FRITSCH (1838-1897) and EDUARD HITZIG (1838-1907) published research findings on the localization of motor functions in the cerebral cortex of the dog. They discovered motor centers only in limited areas of the cerebral cortex and could get specific movements of different muscle groups by activating different cortical regions within such limited areas. This finding, which was soon verified, lent support to Broca's notion of localization of function and spurred physiologists to search vigorously for other motor and sensory centers. Within a short time, evidence supporting the idea of visual centers, auditory centers, and somesthetic centers in the cerebral cortex was presented.

Modern psychology began as physiological psychology with WILHELM WUNDT (1832-1920). Wundt published a book titled *Grundzuge der Physiologischen Psychologie* in 1874. This publication date is sometimes taken to mark the beginning of psychology as an independent science. Wundt used the term "physiological psychology" in the title to distinguish his psychology which emphasized empirical research and an experimental approach from the more prevalent psychology of the day which was primarily philosophical. Wundt's physiological psychology was, therefore, quite different from contemporary physiological psychology; although he wrote chapters on the brain, he was not really much concerned with relationships between psychological and physiological phenomena.

JOHN HUGHLINGS JACKSON (1835-1911), an English neurologist, suggested a doctrine of evolution of the nervous system and of psychological processes. He suggested that the psychological functions most recently achieved through evolution are most easily deranged; in other words, the dissolution of psychological functions is in inverse order of their evolution. Jackson was one of the first neurologists attempting to establish a parallelism between psychophysiological development in general and the findings of neuropathology. He pointed out that positive signs in neurological disorders may result from release of lower nervous centers from the control of higher centers. On the basis of clinical and postmortem studies of epilepsy, aphasia, and paralysis, he concluded that certain cortical areas were concerned with sensory processes, language, and motor activities, thereby providing further support to notions of localization. Jackson studied and described unilateral convulsions restricted to small groups of muscles which may result from an irritative lesion in the contralateral motor cortex; such convulsive behavior is still called Jacksonian epilepsy. Many of Jackson's conceptions were far in advance of his day and have been "rediscovered" many times.

Another Englishman, C. LLOYD MORGAN (1852-1936) strove to offset anthropomorphic tendencies in the interpretation of animal behavior by formulating a principle of parsimony, since known as Lloyd Morgan's Canon. It is: "In no case may we interpret an action as the outcome of the exercise of a higher psychical faculty, if it can be interpreted as the outcome of the exercise of one which stands lower in the psychological scale." In other words, infer the minimum of psychological processes necessary to account for the behavior in question. This conception has proved to be of value to physiological psychology as well as other aspects of psychology in making animals useful tools; the basic idea may also be of value in the interpretation of human behavior.

VI. Twentieth Century Contributions to Physiological Psychology

A. The Early Part of the Twentieth Century

In the early part of the 20th century, as prior to it, the major conceptual and empirical contributions to physiological psychology were made by persons outside the field of psychology. Among the most prominent of these were Sherrington, Pavlov, Adrian, Cannon, Loeb, Child, Cushing, and Berger.

In 1906, CHARLES S. SHERRINGTON (1857-1952) an English neurophysiologist, wrote a book titled *The Integrative Action of the Nervous System.* In it he summarized much of his own experimental research on reflex mechanisms of the spinal cord. The basic thesis of the book is that it is primarily the nervous system which integrates a multicellular animal into a unit organism. He also regarded the reflex as a "convenient abstraction" which may aid in understanding more complex behavior, and he classified receptors into three groups—exteroceptors, interoceptors, and proprioceptors. Sherrington was most foresightful in predicting in 1906 that by combining the methods of comparative psychology (such as maze learning) with methods of experimental physiology, data of importance would accrue regarding brain functioning.

The great Russian physiologist, IVAN P. PAVLOV (1849-1936), spent more than quarter of a century developing, amplifying, and extending his studies of conditioned reaction phenomena. He never considered himself a psychologist and, in fact, seemed to have strong antipathy for psychology in general. He believed that through conditioned reaction phenomena, he could study the dynamics of the brain; in fact, his general theory of behavior was almost exclusively in physiological terms and stressed the significance of activity of the cerebral cortex. His theory of brain changes in conditioning is of historical import for the psychophysiology of learning.

Physiological psychology seems to be a major part of recent and contemporary Russian physiology and psychology. Its orientation is materialistic and deterministic and the Russian psychophysiological tradition has emphasized a visceral-somatic integration rather than a visceral system and a somatic system autonomy which has been more prevalent in western physiology. There are also strong beliefs that the cerebral cortex rather exclusively dominates nervous integration. Besides Pavlov's influence in these directions, writings of IVAN MIKHAILOVICH SECHENOV (1829-1905) have been much responsible for the coalescence of psychology and physiology as one discipline and also for the development of Russian scientific and philosophic thought. Sechenov studied with Mueller, du Bois-Reymond, Helmholtz, Bernard and other outstanding European investigators and on the basis of his own observations developed generalizations to account not only for the physiological but also the psychological properties of the nervous system. His *Reflexes of the Brain* published in 1863 provides the foundational assumptions for the Russian tradition in psychology. VASILY YAKOVLEVICH DANILEVSKY (1852-1939) independently discovered in 1876 that electrical waves could be recorded from the brains of animals; he developed special interest in the cortical representation of visceral functions; and he extended Sechenov's central ideas. NIKOLAI YEVGENEVICH WEDENSKY (1852-1922) whose concepts of inhibition have been useful to both physiology and psychology and ALEXEI ALEXEIVICH UKHTOMSKY (1875-1942), a pupil of Wedensky, whose concept of dominant centers in the nervous system was of interest, are also worthy of mention in connection with the development of contemporary Russian psychophysiology.

EDGAR DOUGLAS ADRIAN (1889-) an English neurophysiologist, has performed brilliant experimental research in electrophysiology and is usually credited with a formulation of the all or nothing principle as applied to the neuron. This all-or-none law states that a nerve fiber supplies the energy for the impulse and is completely discharged when excited at all. In other words, every pulsation of a neuron is maximal; a neuron responds maximally or not at all.

A physiologist at Harvard, WALTER B. CANNON (1871-1945), elaborated the concept of the emergency reaction, developed a theory of emotion, and formulated a notion of homeostasis. The emergency reaction of the sympathetic nervous system is a diffuse complex of bodily activity which serves to mobilize resources of the organism and to prepare the organism for profound expenditure of energy in response to emergency situations. Cannon's theory of emotion stresses the role of the hypothalamus in simultaneously organizing both the experiential and the bodily changes of emotion. The basic idea in homeostasis, which is related also to concepts regarding emotion, is that there is a tendency for internal processes of living organisms to maintain a state of equilibrium or a constant state.

A completely mechanistic psychology, a kind of intellectual descendant of Descartes and of the French mechanists combined with effective application of Morgan's cannon, was developed by JACQUES LOEB (1859-1924). His central concept was the tropism which was defined as a gross specific orienting reaction with respect to particular stimuli. Animals were regarded as automata—mere puppets of external forces. His goal was to explain behavior in terms of principles of chemistry and physics.

21

An American biologist, C. M. CHILD (1869-1954), adduced evidence in support of his physiological gradient concept. This concept holds that in the course of embryological development highest rates of metabolic activity occur at the rostral part and lowest rates in the caudal region with there being an orderly sequence of intermediate gradations between these extremes. Differences in activity at the rostral and caudal parts of the developing organism are described in terms of oxygen consumption, carbon dioxide production, electrical manifestations, heat generation, and susceptibility to toxic conditions.

HARVEY CUSHING (1869-1939), an American neurosurgeon, recorded the effect of parietal lobe stimulation in conscious humans with the cortex exposed. In stimulating the superior portion of the postcentral convolution, sensations were referred by the patient to the lower contralateral extremity, stimulating the middle part resulted in reports of sensations from the trunk and upper extremity and stimulation of the lower portion in sensations from the face. Cushing interpreted these data as suggesting the localization of centers for cutaneous sensitivity.

A Swiss neuropsychiatrist, HANS BERGER (1873-1941), extensively studied the electrical activity of the human brain. He used sensitive recording electrodes fastened to the scalp and by means of lead wires and an amplifying device, was able to record oscillations in electrical activity of the brain in the form of wave-like patterns. This device was called an electroencephalograph, the record an electroencephalogram (both abbreviated EEG), and Berger came to be known as the "Father of Electroencephalography. EEG records have proved to be of value in the diagnosis of brain disease. Berger himself described several kinds of brain wave of interest to the psychologist.

JOHN B. WATSON (1878-1958) proposed a resolution to one aspect of the mind-body problem by discarding consciousness as a concept in psychology. The structural organism and the behavior of the organism were regarded as inseparable. His conceptions are very much responsible for making psychology the study of behavior and for encouraging objectivity of method. This kind of emphasis lead to an approach which fostered the development of modern physiological psychology.

An experimental psychophysiology of learning in animals was begun by SHEPARD IVORY FRANZ (1874-1933) who developed new techniques for assessing the role of brain structures in learning. His work suggested that doctrines of cortical localization were neither complete nor absolute. Franz presented one of the first papers on the neurophysiology of learning; he employed techniques for relating quantitative data of behavior to quantitative data of neurology, and initiated experimental work in the psychophysiology of learning.

KARL S. LASHLEY (1890-1958), an American psychologist, extended Franz's pioneer work and contributed a number of valuable concepts relevant to the psychophysiology of learning. During the 1920s and 1930s and thereafter he published a notable series of papers dealing with cerebral functions in learning; he is best known for his quantitative studies of the relationship between neocortical mass and habit formation. Lashley, probably more than any other single psychologist, made extensive and valuable conceptual and empirical contributions and most advanced our understanding of the psychophysiology of learning.

B. Recent Contributions to Physiological Psychology— Post World War II

As in previous sections of this history, no attempt will be made to present a complete statement of recent contributions. Rather we have selected about half a dozen areas which perhaps are representative of recent contributions and trends.

1. CYBERNETICS AND THE BEHAVIOR OF MACHINES. Cybernetics is the comparative study of organisms and machines with emphasis on communication and control mechanisms. Servomechanisms or feedback mechanisms are devices for maintaining the operation of a system at a prescribed level, or in particular directions. For example, a thermostat operates to maintain a relatively constant temperature in a heating system. Negative feedback enables stability; in this case input does the opposite of output (more input leads to less output and less input to more output). In other words, if temperature goes above the set level it puts in operation a device for reducing temperature, while if temperature falls below the set level, the negative feedback device operates to promote a temperature increase; in that way stability is maintained. Therefore, negative feedback operates as a self-correcting device to maintain constancy, balance, equilibrium, or stability. Positive feedback, on the other hand, leads away from a steady state at a greater and greater

rate. There is, then, progressive disequilibrium and imbalance. In this case, more leads to more and a vicious circle develops. This is true for both men and machines and ultimately positive feedback produces breakdown and destroys both. Analogies and parallels of servomechanisms are found in both men and machines and have led to many stimulating ideas of interest to psychophysiology.

Among the efforts to facilitate understanding of organismic behavior is one of W. Grey Walter, an English physiologist. Walter has constructed a device known as *Machina speculatrix,* a mechanical tortoise, which behaves in some respects like a living organism. It has two amplifiers, two relays, two electric motors, two batteries, and two receptors (a photoreceptor cell and a touch plate) with circuits arranged for "exploratory movements" in darkness and in moderate light; with fully charged batteries the machine is attracted to low illumination and avoids the bright light of its garage. When batteries need recharging however, the bright light of the garage is not avoided but approached. Feeding electrodes engage with the battery charging circuit and its motors are turned off. After recharging the machine is again repelled by light and physical contact of the garage and disengages itself to continue exploratory activities. Thus, with appropriate receiving mechanisms, proper mechanisms for locomotion, and suitable interposed control devices, specific adjustive behavior can be built into a machine. But machine operations are typically much simpler than the behavior of even the simplest living animal. This is their major virtue and their major shortcoming.

2. CEREBRAL CORTEX LOCALIZATION DATA. Wilder Penfield has extensively studied zones of motor and somatic functions of the human cerebral cortex by means of direct stimulation of the brain with tiny electrodes while the patient is awake. Convolutions of hundreds of patients have been explored in this way to determine centers of speech, hearing, and movement. He also has reported locating in the temporal lobe a center for memory recording: "The interpretive cortex has in it a mechanism for instant reactivation of the detailed record of the past." Although many of these findings have not been independently verified, they suggest an exciting approach to acquiring new information on brain function.

3. THE STRESS REACTION. Hans Selye, a Canadian endocrin-

ologist, developed the concept of the General Adaptation Syndrome and has adduced substantial empirical evidence in support of it. A stressor is defined as anything injurious to the organism, either physical or psychological. Various complicated bodily reactions to stress follow in three major stages:

a. The *Alarm Reaction* is the reaction to the provoking agent or stressor; there is a similarity in symptoms of people suffering from various specific illnesses; these symptoms include headache, fever, fatigue, aching muscles, and appetite loss—and are regarded as general symptoms.

b. The *Stage of Resistance* follows if exposure to the stress producing situation continues; the changes developed to resist the particular stressor frequently involve increased activity of the anterior pituitary and the adrenal cortex whose secretions, corticotropin (ACTH) and cortin, respectively, help the organism adjust to stress. With these physiological changes, the processes disturbed during the phase of the alarm reaction tend to disappear and there is a tendency for normal functioning to resume.

c. The *Exhaustion Stage* follows if exposure to the injurious stressor continues too long. The point is reached where the organism can no longer maintain resistance. This is the final phase; the anterior pituitary and adrenal cortex are unable to continue secreting hormones at the increased rate, with the result that the organism can no longer adapt to continuing stress. Many physiological dysfunctions which originally appeared during the alarm reaction begin to reappear. If the stressor continues, death soon occurs.

4. ACTIVATION THEORY OF BEHAVIOR. The activation theory of behavior is particularly concerned with emotion and sleep. The theory developed by Donald B. Lindsley is based on the work of physiologists regarding the role of the reticular formation in arousing the cortex. Behavior ranges from a low level of activation as in deep sleep to a high level of vigorous mobility and responsiveness as in extremes of emotional reactivity. The theory is based somewhat on the research of Moruzzi and Magoun (1949) who found evidence of two kinds of sensory input flowing into the brain: (1) The direct and efficient information kind or cue effects, and (2) a more diffuse and nonspecific kind which may serve an arousal or vigilance function.

5. REWARD AND PUNISHMENT CENTERS IN THE LIMBIC SYS-

TEM. Several years ago, a rat having an electrode buried in the septal area while exploring in an open field was stimulated via the brain-implanted electrode; the experimenter noted that the animal then came to display a peculiar interest in that part of the field, returning frequently to it, and this opened up a relatively new area of research inquiry. A Skinner box was set up permitting rats to depress a lever in order to receive a brain shock and some rats depressed such a self stimulation lever up to 5000 times per hour for several hours without any other obvious reward. This kind of behavior occurred only to stimulation within certain areas of the limbic system and not elsewhere. Later studies demonstrated that direct electrical stimulation of many deep-lying structures of the limbic system seemed to have similar "rewarding" effects in cats and monkeys. There were discovered also areas of the brain, stimulation of which seemed to have a "punishing" effect and led to aversive behavior. Several of the pioneering researches as well as subsequent research elaborations were accomplished by James Olds and his associates.

6. RECENT THEORIES OF THE NEUROLOGY OF LEARNING. After long neglect of the area by psychologists, D. O. Hebb, in recent years, revived interest in theorizing concerning the neurology of perception, motivation and learning by proposing an intriguing original theory. Two basic terms in his theory are the cell assembly and the phase sequence.

The cell assembly is a diffuse structure comprising cells in the cortex and subcortex. It is established through frequently repeated particular stimulation. When this particular stimulation again occurs, the cell assembly is again aroused. Eventually it can go into action as a closed system. The phase sequence is developed by arousal of a series of cell assemblies in succession and the phase sequence is the basis of the thought process.

7. ADVANCES IN BIOCHEMISTRY AND PSYCHOPHARMACOLOGY. In recent years many advances have been made in biochemistry and pharmacology, insofar as these areas relate to the psychological nature of the organism. The biochemistry of the brain and the psychopharmacology of tranquilizers and psychotomimetic drugs might be cited as illustrative of these fascinating fields.

Serotonin (5-hydroxyltryptamine), which causes smooth muscle to contract, has been found in considerable amounts in the brain. Studies suggest that it is concerned with maintaining normal mental function. Also concentrations of an enzyme, cholinesterase, in the brain have been reported as correlated with problem solving behavior in rats.

Tranquilizers or ataractics are compounds that affect emotional behavior; they seem to reduce emotional tension or anxiety. Three which are widely used include (a) reserpine, which is derived from the Rauwolfia serpentina root, (b) chlorpromazine (Thorazine), and (c) meprobamate (Miltown), and reportedly have facilitated treatment of mental disorders, shortened hospital time, and made patients more accessible to treatment. Tranquilizers apparently do not influence functions of the cerebral cortex. They do not produce "clouding of consciousness" nor do they alter normal mechanisms of perception and response to external stimuli. Chlorpromazine, which appears to be the most potent, apparently acts on activating systems of the diencephalon and midbrain.

Psychotomimetic drugs produce profound mental disturbances, including hallucinations and psychotic-like episodes. Representative of such substances are lysergic acid diethylamide (LSD), mescaline, and sernyl.

The mechanisms of action of these drugs and biochemical products have been under active study. It will probably be many years before the locus and manner of operation of these substances is precisely determined.

Summary of the History of Physiological Psychology

Throughout the centuries there have been changing definitions of mind and changing definitions of the field of psychological study. Psychology differentiated gradually from philosophy.

Regarding the term "mind," trends in conceptual, methodological, and knowledge development were cited:

1. Conceptually, notions of mind have changed from reference to something vague and mystical to consideration of a group of phenomena with a tangible referent.

2. Methodologically, the transition has been from techniques in which mind was inaccessible to a group of techniques which permit investigation.

3. From the standpoint of knowledge, progress has been from ignorance to knowledge about "mind" in terms of overt

27

behavior and objective inference based on empirical observation.

As a science, at first psychology apparently had some inferiority attitudes toward the better established sciences; psychologists borrowed methods from physics and chemistry without analyzing them critically. In the course of time, psychology came to develop unique methods of its own. Perhaps in the past the adherence of some psychologists to the physiological area may have stemmed from the desire to be associated with more respectable and better established disciplines. On the other hand, some experimental psychologists have indicated a preference for studying an "empty organism," because there is as yet no certain knowledge of the precise role of the brain in the development of a particular reaction to a particular situation.

Although phrenology is ridiculed, it must be given historical credit for having initiated investigations into cerebral topography and localization which continue to the present.

Among the recurrent themes in the history of psychophysiology are the following: (1) Man is a machine. (2) There are different levels of function of the organism. (3) Some psychological functions seem to be specifiable and localizable insofar as major brain involvements are concerned and others do not seem to be so definitely specifiable.

The outlook for the development of psychophysiology is promising. New theories and methods are being developed and there is much contemporary research effort in the field.

References

The following books on the history of psychology discuss in part contributions to the development of physiological psychology.

Boring, E. G. *A history of experimental psychology.* (2nd ed.) New York: Appleton-Century-Crofts, 1950.

Flugel, J. C. *A hundred years of psychology, 1833-1933.* New York: Macmillan, 1934.

Murphy, G. *Historical introduction to modern psychology.* (Rev. ed.) New York: Harcourt, Brace, 1949.

II

Methods of Physiological Psychology

Physiological psychology is concerned with relationships between the psychological and biological nature of the organism. In psychophysiological research, biological characteristics within the organism may be manipulated as independent variables or assessed as dependent variables. For example, the role of various parts of the brain in learning, thinking, speech behavior, sensory functions, or motor activity may be systematically altered as independent variables by a variety of procedures; likewise the effects of patterns of stimulation or behavior on various dependent variables such as the electroencephalogram, or adrenal secretion, or amplitude of cardiac contraction, or neural conduction rate may be evaluated.

An implicit premise of physiological psychology is that a living organism, or an organismic process is best understood by taking it apart—by dissecting it, isolating it, or otherwise analyzing it into smaller components, such as reflexes, nerve impulses, changes in blood chemistry, changes in endocrine gland activity and the like. From this point of view, more complex and elaborate phenomena, then, are to be understood in terms of the simpler.

In general, science advances through an interaction of theory, method, and empirical finding. Each serves to develop, refine and improve the other. However, it is rather infrequent in physiological psychology research that implications of a general theory are tested. Experiments more frequently originate from suggestions of earlier experiments; the hypotheses investigated, therefore, may be limited, unrelated, and share no systematic rationale. Nevertheless, progress has been made in physiological psychology, and it is a thriving and rapidly developing field.

Certain research instruments in physiological psychology as in other fields serve as expansions, extensions, and amplifications of man's senses. These tools permit more adequate exploration of the world; successes and failures in the search to discover new knowledge help determine ways in which the tools may be modified and sharpened to improve acuity. The methods employed in a field of research endeavor are best understood in terms of the goals of that field. It will be convenient to discuss first basic biological methods, then clinical methods, and finally experimental methods.

I. Basic Biological Methods

The plethora of techniques for investigating biological phenomena do not lend themselves to a comprehensive survey. Since the nervous system is one of the biological systems in which physiological psychology has a particular interest, special attention will be paid to it. Perhaps at the outset it is also appropriate to point out that there are several sources of confusion which may make for difficulty in studying the nervous system.

(1). First of all, there are problems relating to the names of nervous structures. Components of the nervous system have been specified in many ways, viz., in terms of shape, color, function, discoverer, or location of the structure. Thus, there are the olives and the pyramids; the red nucleus and the substantia nigra; the olfactory tract and the auditory area; the column of Goll, the stripe of Genarri, Wernicke's area, and the fissure of Rolando; the dorsomedian sulcus and the ventral spinothalamic tract.

(2). Second, there may be double, triple, or even quadruple names for a structure. For example, the colliculi, the tectum, and the corpora quadrigemina all refer to essentially the same midbrain structure; the visual area, the striate area, and Brodmann's area 17 are for all practical purposes the same.

(3). Third, there are unsystematic groupings of structures. For example, the medulla is part of the myelencephalon (pons and medulla), part of the rhombencephalon (cerebellum and medulla), in part is included as a component of the reticular formation, and also is part of the brain stem (all parts of the brain except the cerebrum and the cerebellum). Most structures of the nervous systems have synonyms and approximate synonyms and also may be specified descriptively in a variety of ways. For the novice, then, there are many opportunities for confusion.

A. Gross Observation

Observations of gross structures of the nervous system may be specified in terms of size, shape, color and position of structure. Several pairs of biological terms are used to indicate position—cranial-caudal (head-tail), anterior-posterior (front-rear), dorsal-ventral (back side and belly side), medial-lateral (toward the midline and toward the side), proximal-distal (with reference to an appendage, area nearest attachment to the trunk and area furthest away from attachment).

In diagrams of interior structures, it is convenient to designate sections as coronal or frontal (section dividing an organ into front and rear parts), sagittal or median (section dividing an organ into right and left parts), and transverse or horizontal (section separating an organ into top and bottom parts) in order to convey clearly information about relative position of structures.

B. Microscopic Observation

Microscopic observation permits study of the finer details and the more minute anatomy. This is not readily accomplished in living organisms. Thin transparent sections are prepared by a variety of techniques and stained to permit most precise observation of particular structures. With regard to neurons (nerve cells), Nissl stain which involves the use of such substances as cresyl violet, toluidine blue or methylene blue, stains certain neural granules a bluish color. The Golgi method involves staining neurofibrils (long thin *fibrils* extending throughout nerve cell body and fiber substance) with solutions of silver salts such as silver nitrate which, when absorbed by nerve cells, produces a metallic silver deposit on neurofibrils. The Weigert method employs osmic acid which colors myelin black and leaves the axon unstained. The Marchi method which employs potassium dichromate permits staining degenerating myelin fibers.

Although staining does emphasize particular microscopic structures, there are some major problems: (1). In the first place, staining permits efficient detection of only one part of the structure; the resulting description is therefore *incomplete*.

(2). In the second place, since only one part is efficiently detected the description may be *distorted;* there may be an overlay of many kinds of fibers and cell bodies in the same general area which are not described. (3). Structures may be modified and distorted by the process of staining as well as by other processes employed in preparing such structures for study.

Despite certain limitations, these various techniques permit acquisition of information on biological structure. Physiological psychology, however, is concerned with relationships between biological structure and behavior.

II. Clinical Methods

The methods used in the medical and psychological clinic are employed to elicit information of practical value from the standpoint of the patient's welfare. They are not used with the same goals as the methods of the research laboratory. The research scientist is primarily concerned with acquiring new knowledge for the sake of improving understanding—without any necessary concern about practical application of his findings. The clinician is primarily concerned with eliciting information which will be of help in diagnosis and therapy; he endeavors to assist a particular patient—to facilitate that patient's cure. However, as an incidental by-product of clinical activity, the clinician may make original discoveries of relationships—may expand general knowledge in a field of science—may suggest intriguing hypotheses for more rigorous laboratory evaluation —and all of these contributions while they may not particularly help the patient, are likely to be of considerable value to research science. Nevertheless, the primary goal of the clinician is to institute remedial procedures, to aid the patient, to produce improvement in the patient's functioning.

Approximately half of the first admissions to mental hospitals are diagnosed in the general realm of "Organic Brain Disorder." Such disorder is typically accompanied by a variety of symptoms of interest to psychology including disorientation, unusual affective behavior, and impairment in comprehension, learning, remembering, judging, planning, and reasoning functions. Sometimes these disorders are dichotomized; *acute* organic brain disorders refer to conditions in which the symptoms are temporary and the physical change is reversible while *chronic* brain disorders refer to conditions in which the symptoms are likely to be persistent and the physical change in the brain (i.e., damage) is permanent.

A. General Clinical Study Procedures

Perhaps three general procedures of clinical research study of interest to physiological psychology can be outlined. In each case, the attempt of the research-oriented clinician is to evaluate relationships between the biological nature of the patient and his psychological functioning. Again our emphasis is on a system of great importance in behavioral integration and, therefore, of special interest to the psychologist, the nervous system.

1. PROCEDURES FOR STUDYING ACCIDENTAL DESTRUCTION OF TISSUE IN THE NERVOUS SYSTEM. Subject matter within this category includes injuries due to vehicular accidents, industrial accidents, and war. Most frequently the causal agent is mechanical: Concussion refers to damage resulting from a violent jar to the skull or spinal column in which brain or spinal cord circulation is disrupted, perhaps due to rupture of small blood vessels in the brain or cord as a consequence of a blow. Contusion refers to a bruising of the surface of the brain due to its compression against the cranium. Laceration is an actual rupture or tearing of brain tissue. This group of procedures is concerned with relating concussion, contusion, and laceration to particular symptoms and other behavioral changes.

2. PROCEDURES FOR STUDYING PATHOLOGICAL CHANGES IN THE CENTRAL NERVOUS SYSTEM. The pathological changes referred to are the effects of circulatory problems, biological infection, chemical conditions, and pathological growths. Circulatory problems include blood clots in arteries supplying the brain, intracranial hemorrhages, and cerebral arteriosclerosis. Biological infections produce disorders such as general paresis, juvenile paresis, and cerebral syphilis, all of which are due to a protozoon organism, the treponema pallidum, epidemic encephalitis which is due to filterable virus, and epidemic cerebrospinal meningitis which is caused by a bacterial organism, the meningococcus. Chemical conditions may be due to the inhalation of toxic substances such as lead or manganese dust or carbon monoxide, to nutritional deficiencies such as lack of vitamin B complex, to endocrine dysfunctions such as exces-

sive thyroid secretion or undersecretion of the adrenal cortex, as well as a variety of other metabolic disturbances. Pathological growths refer to neoplasms—tissue growths independent of the normal rate of development which serve no physiological function and may actually interfere with normal functioning. Tumors within the brain are illustrative. Pathological growths outside the nervous system, for example in glands or in the circulatory system, may also profoundly influence behavior. This group of procedures is concerned with relating circulatory difficulties, biological infections, chemical conditions, and pathological growths to behavioral changes.

3. PROCEDURES FOR STUDYING THE EFFECTS OF NEUROSURGERY. Sometimes surgery is employed as a treatment technique; effects of such surgery may be studied in the altered behavior of the patient in the attempt to ascertain relationships between biological structure and psychological processes. Surgical procedures may be used for purposes of removing a bone fragment or other agent imbedded in the brain, to sever connections between one part of the brain and another, or perhaps to remove a pathological growth. An operation requiring removal of an entire lobe of the cerebrum is called a lobectomy.

Since 1935 a variety of brain surgical techniques have been especially employed in the treatment of psychological disorders; collectively, these are now known as psychosurgery. Historically, one of the first of these procedures was bilateral prefrontal lobotomy, a technique which involves severing fiber connections between the frontal lobes and the thalamus. Leukotomy is a synonym for lobotomy. Another important psychosurgical technique is topectomy, in which one or more specific areas of the cortex are removed.

B. The Neurological Examination

One of the basic means of securing clinical information is the neurological examination. The neurological examination is based on knowledge of the anatomy and physiology of the nervous system. Tests are employed to ascertain normal functions, loss of function, or absence of function. Although many of the tests are crude, they are nevertheless of practical value. The neurological examination is not considered a finished technique. Rather it is conceived as in constant flux in the direction of improvement. Data from laboratory experimentation are continually being transferred in modified form to the clinical situation so that refinement in neurological diagnosis is a continuous and progressive process.

From the neurologist's viewpoint, assuming that there is a structural pathology—and frequently, of course, the examination is intended to differentiate functional from organic disorders—the attempt is made to answer three questions: 1. Where is the lesion? 2. What is the lesion? 3. What causes the lesion?

Much information can be elicited via free recitation by the patient and by questioning—especially definite and detailed "subjective" evidences of disordered function which are difficult to obtain in other ways. Sometimes information concerning heredity, family health, early development, drug habits, previous illnesses, disabilities, and infections is not otherwise available. The manner, attitude, general behavior, especially speech and locomotor behavior, and facts regarding the nature of the illness, e.g., whether chronic or remitting, whether of sudden or gradual onset, may be of value.

The conduct and direction of the neurological examination much depends upon interview data; it also depends on the neurologist's ingenuity in developing and using various clinical tests. One systematic way of proceeding involves a check of cranial and spinal nerves, then sensory and motor systems, and finally higher psychological functions.

To illustrate: The efficiency of cranial nerve I, the olfactory nerve, can be assessed by using common volatile substances with characteristic odors such as peppermint, oil of cloves, soap, coffee and tobacco; the operation of cranial nerve II, the optic nerve, can be assessed by employing a Snellen-type chart for visual acuity and employing confrontation methods of perimetry for continuity in the visual field, as well as other techniques; the functioning of cranial nerves III, IV, and VI, the oculomotor, the trochlear, and the abducens nerves which regulate eye movements can be assessed by testing eye movements, such as rotation and convergence and a variety of reflexes; the adequacy of cranial nerve V, the trigeminal, sensory and motor to the head region is determined by using a variety of stimuli such as pressure with pieces of cotton or pin prickings and various movements of the face. Similar techniques are utilized for assessing other cranial nerves as well as the spinal nerves.

Motor functioning is variously assessed—motor tonus by slowly and passively moving the patient's limbs to determine hypotonicity, hypertonicity, and atonicity. A variety of signs suggest cerebellar problems—unsteadiness and tendency to fall to one side, decomposition of movement, intention tremor, dysmetria, the rebound phenomenon, and adiadochokinesis. Some kinds of convulsions suggest lesions in the motor area of the cortex. Choreiform movements, athetoid movements, and ballism often suggest disturbances in the basal nuclei. A variety of reflexes provide information on the intactness of the spinal cord and the Babinski response may be an indicator of pyramidal tract lesions. The Romberg sign refers to a swaying of the body which occurs when the patient stands with eyes shut and feet close together. It is typically regarded as an indicator of proprioceptive deficiency rather than as an injury to central nervous motor structures.

Higher psychological functions may be assessed (1) by checking recall and its deficiencies—amnesia, (2) by the use of standard intelligence tests, (3) by analysis of handwriting for such characteristics as irregular size, tremulousness, deletion or repetition of letters, wavering lines, and (4) by consideration of articulation problems. Dysarthria including slow, tremulous, drawling, hesitant and slurring speech may occur. In general paresis, difficulties with the consonants "l" and "r" are especially apparent and may be evaluated by observation of the patient's repetition of such phrases as "truly rural," "thirty-third artillery brigade," and "round the rugged rock the ragged rascal ran"; there are also difficulties with long or complex words or phrases such as "Methodist Episcopal."

C. Special Diagnostic Methods

Among the special diagnostic methods often employed in the attempt to ascertain nervous system pathology are angiography, spinal fluid analysis, pneumoencephalography, ventriculography, electroencephalography, and ophthalmoscopy. Certain elementary information about bodily functions is necessary in order to appreciate those techniques.

The circulatory system transports oxygen, ingested foods and hormones as well as performing many other functions. The system consists of a pumping mechanism, the heart, and a number of tubules directing blood away from the heart, the

36

arteries, others directing blood back toward the heart, the veins, and interposed between the two, very tiny tubules supplying abundantly all parts of the body, the capillaries. Capillary networks are extensive in the central nervous system, especially in the gray matter. Deficiencies in circulation and consequent deprivation of oxygen will begin to kill nervous system cells within a few minutes. Cranial cavity blood supply is accomplished by means of the common carotid and vertebral arteries: The common carotid artery divides into the external and internal carotid arteries; the internal carotid in turn becomes the inferior and middle cerebral arteries. The vertebral arteries join at the medulla to form the basilar artery which in turn becomes the posterior cerebral arteries. Each of the two posterior cerebral arteries is joined by a tiny branch to the corresponding middle cerebral arteries and thereby forms the arterial circle or the circle of Willis. This permits continued circulation of blood in the brain even though a major artery to it may be blocked or damaged.

A system of cavities or ventricles in the brain and connections between those cavities makes up the ventricular system. The lateral ventricles which are largely in the cerebral hemispheres communicate by means of the interventricular foramina with the third ventricle in the vicinity of the thalamus and hypothalamus which communicates via the aqueduct of Sylvius with the fourth ventricle in the region of the pons, medulla, and cerebellum which in turn connects with the central canal leading downward through the core of the medulla and spinal cord.

Surrounding the brain and spinal cord are the meninges, three coverings, the outermost or dura mater a tough fibrous membrane, the middle or arachnoid mater which is a more weblike structure, and the innermost membrane or pia mater which is closely applied to the surface of the brain and spinal cord. The subarachnoid spaces are openings below the arachnoid mater. There is an aperture which communicates between the fourth ventricle and the subarachnoid spaces.

Now a fluid, the cerebrospinal fluid, flows within the ventricles and the subarachnoid spaces. This fluid originates from a complex of tiny blood vessels for the most part within the lateral ventricles which are known as the choroidal plexuses. It is an almost protein-free liquid and it circulates from the lateral to the third and then the fourth ventricles where it makes egress into the subarachnoid spaces and eventually is returned from them to the circulatory system. A pressure gradient is largely responsible for this circulation.

This means, then, that the central nervous system is well protected by (1) a boney framework, the skull and spinal column, (2) a set of membranes, the meninges, and (3) a liquid cushion provided by the cerebrospinal fluid.

1. ANGIOGRAPHY. Angiography is a technique for determining abnormal vascular patterns—for ascertaining interruptions or blocks of blood flow and shifts in the position of blood vessels due to tumors or other lesions. Blood vessels are visualized by injecting radiopaque dye into an artery in the neck, either the common carotid or the vertebral, and then making x-ray photographs as the dye circulates through cranial blood vessels. Vascular pathology, including vascular occlusions and ruptures, may thereby be detected.

2. CEREBROSPINAL FLUID ANALYSIS. Since the spinal cord terminates at about the third lumbar level of the spinal column, and since the meninges continue below this level, it is possible to thrust a hollow needle between the third and fourth lumbar vertebrae and penetrate the meninges into the subarachnoid space without damaging the spinal cord. By attaching a manometer to the penetrating needle, cerebrospinal fluid pressure can be measured. With abnormal conditions, such as pathological growths or obstructions, there may be unusual changes in cerebrospinal fluid pressure.

Information indicating central nervous system pathology sometimes can be obtained by sampling and analyzing the cerebrospinal fluid obtained at this point. Although normally clear, the fluid may become cloudy with the presence of proteins, salts, or other substances; it may contain blood which is often indicative of central nervous system hemorrhage; there may be white blood corpuscles present suggesting infection or inflammation, the type and number of them serving as a clue to the nature and variety of the condition; there may be microorganisms present.

In hydrocephalus excess cerebrospinal fluid accumulates in the brain, usually due to interference with circulation. When the condition occurs in early infancy before skull bones are fully calcified, the pressure from within causes the brain to expand and thereby also causes an expansion of the skull. In the process, skull bones are thinned and the brain is compressed between the tremendous fluid pressure from within and the skull bones from without. There is, therefore, interference with normal development and often idiocy results. Death may result if pressure interferes with vital brain stem processes.

3. PNEUMOENCEPHALOGRAPHY. Pneumoencephalography involves introducing air at the lumbar puncture to permit visualization of the cranial cavity; via x-ray photography, the position of a mass interfering with normal cerebrospinal fluid flow may be determined.

4. VENTRICULOGRAPHY. Ventriculography involves the preparation of a radiogram of the ventricles injected with air via a needle after a small hole has been drilled in the skull cap.

5. ELECTROENCEPHALOGRAPHY. The electroencephalograph (EEG) is an instrument devised for detecting electrical activity of the brain. The apparatus consists of recording electrodes which are positioned on the scalp, lead wires from the electrodes proceeding to an amplifier, and then to an ink-writer or similar recording device. The resulting graphic record is called an electroencephalogram (also abbreviated EEG); the abscissa represents the time and the ordinate represents amplitude or voltage. It is the passage of the sum of the potentials of millions of neural cells through the skull, muscles, blood vessels and skin which are recorded.

Brain waves vary in frequency (duration), amplitude (voltage), and complexity (wave form or contour). Frequency is typically expressed in units per second and amplitude in microvolts. Complexity is considered in terms of Fourier's theorem, viz., any continuous sequence of complex undulations may be analyzed and reduced to a series of sine waves of stated frequencies and amplitudes.

A simple, convenient, and generally employed classification uses frequency as the major variable. According to it, a variety of common wave forms may be distinguished as follows.

a. ALPHA WAVES: These have a frequency of 8 to 12 units per second, with the mean being approximately 10. This is regarded as a typical or fundamental wave. Under standard conditions of minimum stimulation with normal adults, awake and relaxed, this rhythm is relatively stable and persistent.

b. BETA WAVES: Beta waves have a frequency of about 18 to 35 per second with a mean of about 25.

c. GAMMA WAVES: Gamma waves are relatively rapid with a frequency of 35 to 60 per second.

d. DELTA WAVES: Delta waves have a frequency of ½ to 3 per second.

e. THETA WAVES: Theta waves have a frequency of 4 to 7 per second.

f. KAPPA WAVES: Kappa waves have a frequency which is about the same as alpha, i.e., approximately 10 per second; but the voltages are much smaller and they occur under different conditions.

g. SLEEP SPINDLES: These have a frequency of between 14 and 17; sometimes they are called fast alphas or slow betas; they typically occur during light sleep.

Another classification emphasizes the unique distinguishing characteristics of brain waves; according to it, one may talk about saw-tooth waves, sharp spikes, spike and dome patterns, among other idiosyncratic wave features.

Delta waves seem to be a very useful sign of brain tissue pathology. Abnormality in rate, amplitude, or wave form in general, is often worth further investigation; about 90% of all brain tumors apparently are reflected in abnormal electro-encephalograms.

Brain wave patterns also serve as indicators of epilepsy. Very slow or very fast brain waves are 20 times more common in epileptics than in controls. The spike-dome pattern, an alternation of slender, sharply-pointed waves with more gradual "flat-top" waves, is an indicator of petit mal epilepsy and occurs during petit mal attacks. Hyperventilation for two or three minutes frequently produces abnormal waves not discovered during normal breathing; it also tends to increase accuracy in the diagnosis of epilepsy.

Among the factors which influence the EEG are the following: (1) The position of electrodes with respect to the focal center for specific waves. (2) The age of the patient; at birth and in early life the antecedents of the adult alpha are slower and more irregular. (3) The degree of sensory stimulation, e.g., alpha waves tend to disappear in the presence of strong light. (4) Level of waking; during lesser hypnagogic states, theta waves often occur; in deeper hypnagogic states, sleep spindles may occur. (5) Mental set, thinking, and problem solving activities; under these circumstances alpha waves tend to be depressed; sometimes beta or kappa waves appear. (6) Individual anatomical differences especially in brain structure; these may relate to characteristic distinctive patterns for particular individuals.

Considerable evidence exists that activity of the brain stem reticular formation alters brain wave patterns; apparently the ascending reticular activating system mediates arousal reactions with desynchronization or flattening of the EEG.

6. OPHTHALMOSCOPY. The ophthalmoscope is a perforated mirror used for examining the interior of the eye; with it, all parts of the retina may be seen. The retina is the only part of the nervous system which can be seen directly in the intact living human; embryologically, the retina is part of the brain.

Medial to the macula lutea is a whitish area, the optic disk or blind spot, from which small arteries and veins are dispersed throughout the retina. The optic disk and these vessels may reflect certain pathological changes. For example, compression of retinal blood vessels as a consequence of intracranial pressure may seriously interfere with circulation in the retina. With a rise in venous pressure, circulatory fluid is forced out of the capillaries and permeates the retina, especially in the region of the optic disk; the disk, thereby, becomes swollen or "choked." Apparently the amount of choking is a fair index of the amount of increase in intracranial pressure. The disk area appears to be quite sensitive; effects of pathological processes may be seen clearly; the ophthalmoscope is, therefore, a valuable diagnostic tool.

D. Special Therapeutic Methods

1. DRUG TECHNIQUES. A variety of drugs have been used in the attempt to influence psychological processes. Thousands of research investigations have been accomplished concerning the psychological effects of common drugs such as caffeine, nicotine, and alcohol. In more recent years, the effects of many other drugs, especially those used in the treatment of behavior disorders, have been extensively studied—particularly the tranquilizers and stimulants. Tranquilizers such as chlorpromazine, or meprobamate, or reserpine, are medically prescribed to overcome emotional disturbances, including anxiety and manic

excitement; stimulants such as iproniazid are prescribed to combat depression.

2. PSYCHOSURGERY. Psychosurgery refers to a variety of brain surgical techniques employed for the purpose of facilitating psychological processes and personality adjustment. On the basis of information concerning human beings with frontal lobe damage including tumorous growth, on the basis of frontal lobe surgery, and on the basis of experimentation with animals, Egas Moniz in a Lisbon (Portugal) hospital initiated a surgical technique for the treatment of behaviorally disturbed patients who were otherwise without any obvious brain damage. The surgery was used with patients on whom other procedures had been attempted unsuccessfully—on patients regarded as hopelessly incurable—and was regarded as a method of the last resort. In 1935 Moniz interrupted fibers projecting to the frontal lobes in 20 patients and reported seven recoveries, seven improvements, and six unimproved. Encouraged by the results reported in his monograph published in 1936, the operation was instituted in neuropsychiatric centers throughout the world. The operation is known as bilateral prefrontal lobotomy. Bilateral prefrontal lobotomy in recent years has disappeared almost completely. Certain drugs seem to produce somewhat similar conditions without imposing extensive brain damage.

Topectomy, a surgical procedure originated later for the treatment of behavioral disorders, involves ablation of small specific areas of the cerebral cortex.

Stereotaxic surgery was developed largely by an American researcher, Robert H. Clarke in the London laboratory of Victor Horsley. The Horsley-Clarke stereotaxic instrument is a metal cage of aluminum rods in a frame into which the skull is positioned. Through a small aperture previously drilled in the skull, a needle tipped with an electrode and directed down toward the top of the skull is mounted on a sliding carriage which moves in three planes and its position is regulated by knob turning. The needle may be driven through brain tissue to a certain level at which point it is possible to destroy specific internal structures such as a nucleus in the hypothalamus. For example, it is possible to destroy a thalamic nucleus from which fibers ascend and break into a spray on the way to the cortex. Such a procedure would be termed a thalectomy. The technique in modified form is useful for imbedding both stimulating and recording electrodes and for injecting drugs directly into deeper parts of the brain. By means of a hollow hypodermic needle it is also possible to implant a radon seed—a measured amount of radium—for the treatment of tumor.

Ultrasonic irradiations in millions of vibrations per second can be focussed like light waves and are capable of destroying nervous tissue without doing visible damage to other parts of the body. Ultrasonic radiation surgery involves the use of two half-threshold beams that may be intersected on target. Neither beam alone is sufficiently powerful to do serious damage, but together at the point of intersection they can produce graded subcortical lesions in very specific areas.

E. Representative Clinical Material

For the sake of supplementing information on clinical method, a few paragraphs are provided below on the kinds of behavior pathology which might be of interest to the physiological psychologist.

1. PHINEAS P. GAGE—THE AMERICAN CROWBAR CASE

At Cavendish, Vermont on September 13, 1848, Phineas P. Gage, a 25-year-old foreman for the Rutland and Burlington Railroad while working closely in an excavation was the victim of an explosion in which a tamping iron was driven through the left side of his face and emerged from the top right side of his skull. Convulsive movements occurred almost immediately. He spoke after a few moments, was carried to the road, onto an oxcart, and about three-quarters of a mile to his hotel where he got out himself, walked up a long flight of stairs, and put himself to bed. He recovered and was apparently in good physical health for many years thereafter. However, he is reported to have changed from an active, steady, alert workman to a restless, adventurous, unreliable person; he became an impatient, obstinate, grossly profane and undependable person. One interesting aspect of this case is that apparently it is possible to destroy a vast quantity of brain tissue without necessary or conspicuous immediate loss in sensory processes, motor processes, speech, or consciousness.

2. GENERAL PARESIS

General paresis, also called dementia paralytica, is an organic brain disorder due to spirochaetes of syphilis; it is estimated that less than 3% of untreated syphilitics become paretic. Paresis is characterized by progressive personality and intellectual deterioration. A wide range of signs and symptoms are frequently found in general paresis, although they are not peculiar to it. Among these are: (1) the Argyll-Robertson pupil, characterized by irregularity in pupillary size and in which the pupillary reflex to light is either sluggish or absent, (2) marked tremor of the lips and tongue, (3) disturbance in speech functions including a slowness in speech and a slurring of words, (4) illegible writing, (5) locomotor ataxia—a shuffling incoordinate gait, (6) convulsive seizures, and (7) muscular weakness. In untreated cases there is relatively rapid deterioration with death occurring usually within about three years. Behaviorally, the disorder is characterized by a gradual loss of interest, disintegration of personal habits, and impaired memory, comprehension, and judgment.

3. LEAD PSYCHOSIS

Lead psychosis which typically results from prolonged exposure to lead fumes and dust producing brain damage is characterized by symptoms ranging from fatigue, listlessness, and irritability to insomnia, restlessness, anxiety, tremor, and hallucinations.

In cases such as those indicated above, the physiological psychologist is interested in ascertaining concomitance between symptoms and organic damage.

F. Some Typical Conclusions of Clinical Research Investigations

On the basis of clinical research findings, a number of generalizations may be made. A few of these are formulated below with some remarks concerning them. The generalizations specified are not in any way systematically related, but are representative of generalizations permissible from findings of the clinic.

1. Some visible changes in a brain *may* be unrelated to how it operates. Extensive degenerative brain changes have been observed in postmortems of people who have functioned very well throughout life. Also apparently well-developed brains, free of obvious pathology, are sometimes found in the

44

seriously mentally retarded and in extremely disturbed persons. For example, there seem to be no systematic relationships between evidences of brain pathology, macroscopic or microscopic, and the functional psychoses, including schizophrenia on the basis of our present state of knowledge. Often, then, it is not possible to ascertain from anatomical examination of the brain, how it has operated.

2. In conditions of organic pathology which affect the central nervous system of man and give rise to behavioral disturbances, the nature of the symptomatology depends in part at least on the nature of the lesion:

a. LOCATION OF THE LESION: Lesions in sensory and motor regions of the cortex lead to interference in sensory and motor functions, respectively.

b. SIZE OF THE LESION: In some cases, at least, there is a direct relationship between size of the lesion and extent of deficit. For example, the greater the extent of damage to the visual area of the cortex, the greater the area of visual insensitivity; with complete visual area destruction bilaterally, there is complete blindness bilaterally.

c. CONSTANCY OF THE LESION: The effects of fixed and definite lesions are different from the effects of progressive and expanding lesions.

d. DESTRUCTIVE OR IRRITATIVE LESION: Destructive lesions may lead to loss of function while irritative lesions may lead to special activation of function. For example, destruction of tissue in the auditory area leads to hearing interference while irritative lesions there may produce auditory hallucinations; destruction of part of a motor area may lead to a partial loss of motor function while irritation may produce convulsive movements.

Behavioral consequences may depend in part on the nature of the lesion; however, symptoms may also depend much on the nature of the prepathological personality of the patient and perhaps in some cases not very much on the lesion.

3. Other things being equal, with expanding central nervous system lesions, behavior becomes progressively less well integrated.

a. Other things being equal, with nonexpanding lesions, behavior may show improvement in organization and efficiency in time.

b. Other things being equal, generally nonexpanding lesions early in life have less effect than lesions of the same size after maturity.

G. Evaluation of the Clinical Method

The major value of the clinical method is that the data are based on human populations and this eliminates the problem of interspecies generalization of findings. However, meaningful and reliable data are difficult to obtain. There are a number of special problems of clinical method which contribute to this difficulty.

1. LACK OF RANDOMNESS AND SMALL SAMPLE SIZE. Individuals in the clinical situation are not randomly chosen and probably are not representative of the human population generally. Furthermore, samples are likely to be small, i.e., to involve only a few cases—in some instances only a single case—and there is likely to be difficulty in finding an appropriate control group. Sometimes reports of clinical research disclose no control group or a poorly planned or inadequate group. In any case, the clinical population is obtained "opportunistically."

2. PATHOLOGY IN THE SAMPLE. Findings in the clinical situation are based on "pathological" groups, i.e., the subjects in clinical samples display behavioral or structural pathology or both.

3. INADEQUATE INITIAL OBSERVATION. In the clinical situation, there often is no careful preparation for the observations that may later prove to be most meaningful from the standpoint of research science. The initial observations must be made when the patient is required to come to the clinic (e.g., accident or unexpected physical trauma) or when he chooses to do so. In emergency situations, or when the clinical staff is overloaded with work, it may not be possible to make as thorough an examination as ordinarily would be desired.

4. LACK OF LESION CONTROL. There is a lack of control regarding lesions. Lesions are not likely to be neat, precise, clear-cut and confined to particular regions of special psychological or neurological interest. Rather, they are apt to involve various areas and levels of the brain. But lesion size—or some other lesion characteristic—is often the independent variable requiring careful control.

5. ABSENCE OF PREPATHOLOGY PSYCHOLOGICAL ASSESSMENT.

46

With a clinical population, often there is no base line of the individual's normal performance for comparison purposes, that is, one does not know how the individual performed before brain damage. For example, suppose a patient on a standard test of general intelligence after extensive cortical damage receives a score in the range immediately below the average range: What does the score mean? Obviously, it is difficult to know if one does not have objective records obtained *prior to* brain damage. If there is a lack of knowledge of prepathological psychological functioning (e.g., knowledge of preinjury personality, its nature and stability, temperament, etc.) there are almost insurmountable problems concerning whether or not changes have occurred and, if so, ascertaining the directions and magnitudes of such changes. The prepathological characteristics conceivably may relate to the nature of postpathological disturbance, with the lesion having little direct effect.

6. COMPLICATION OF COEXISTING PSYCHOGENIC SYMPTOMS. Some symptoms which are purely psychogenic or functional may suggest brain lesions. For example, memory loss may be due to lack of motivation, the result of retroactive influences, or an aspect of a conversion reaction. Also physical causes such as fever or drug conditions or fatigue may lead to symptoms suggestive of brain lesion. There is a problem of isolating such effects from those directly attributable to brain pathology.

7. PROBLEM OF ADAPTATION TO AND RECOVERY FROM BRAIN DAMAGE EFFECTS. By the time the patient comes to clinical attention, adaptation to a deficiency caused by brain damage can be considerable so that the deficiency may escape ready detection. Also, there may be "recovery" from the effects of lesion prior to receiving clinical attention.

8. COMPLICATION OF SECONDARY OR INDIRECT PSYCHOGENIC SYMPTOMS. Complex behavioral changes may occur as a result of interaction between brain damage and functional symptoms. A combination of neurotic symptoms or functional psychotic symptoms may coexist with other symptoms more fundamentally due to structural damage. Loss of motivation or changes in affective tone may be a function of the fact that there has been personal injury, but in no way unique to the fact that the injury involves brain damage. Recognition of capacity loss, worry about personal relations, and concern with economic

problems may likewise lead to behavioral aberrations which are therefore *indirectly,* not directly, related to brain damage.

9. DIFFICULTY IN ESTIMATING LESION MAGNITUDE IN THE CLINICAL SITUATION. There is considerable difficulty in estimating the magnitude and nature of brain damage at the time a clinical research investigation is being conducted. The standard clinical techniques, e.g., EEG, ventriculography, pneumoencephalography, etc., are indirect, that is they are not based on direct observation of the brain, Like all indirect techniques, they are subject to much error. Likewise, each instrument gets at only a limited number of aspects of structure or function, and each therefore is less complete than desired.

10. LACK OF INFORMATION ON LESION LOCUS. Clinical investigators may never learn where the brain lesion is located precisely. There may be no very good indication disclosed by psychological or by medical tests—merely evidence highly suggestive of brain damage.

11. LACK OF POSTMORTEM DATA. Postmortem examination to confirm or challenge earlier diagnosis is relatively rare. Verification of brain damage is a problem. Typically, the brain is unavailable for autopsy. Or if it is available, the likelihood is that information will not get back to the clinical facility which earlier was concerned with appraisal of the damage. Certainly this is probable if the patient lives for 20 or 30 or 40 years after the brain injury, or if he moves to another city or state.

12. SPECIAL PROBLEMS OF POSTMORTEM LESION EVALUATION. Even with postmortem examination data, formidable problems exist of relating brain lesions to performance aberrations. Let us say that postmortem data are transmitted to an appropriate clinical facility on a clinical research subject who passed away five years after observation and notation of his symptoms. The problem of relating deficit five years previous to the observed postmortem lesion is difficult if the lesion was an expanding one. Or if there are several lesions, it may be difficult to ascertain which occurred about five years ago and which prior to or subsequent to that time. And of course, there are other problems, concerning to what extent "compensation" had occurred for the lesion.

The above may be representative, if not exhaustive, of the problems involved in getting information of relevance to physiological psychology by the clinical method.

In summary, the major criticisms of the clinical research method are that: (1) It is opportunistic. (2) It involves a lack of precision and control. (3) There is a lack of verification evidence regarding the nature and magnitude of lesions.

III. Experimental Methods

Significant questions are raised, then, about clinical data and their value. The need for more precise and better controlled methods is met by experimentation. An experiment is a systematic series of controlled observations which are repeatable and verifiable. The research investigator manipulates circumstances and provides occasion for the event which he is prepared to observe.

Experimental procedures in physiological psychology may involve human or infrahuman organisms. Infrahuman organisms are a fruitful source for the most precise data.

According to the doctrine of evolution, organisms can be arranged on a dendritic scale from simple to complex. Simple organisms are those composed of relatively few cells which are relatively unspecialized; more complex organisms are constituted of a greater number of cells many of which are structurally specialized. Presumably, the more complex developed from the simpler over the course of eons of time. According to evolutionary doctrine, organisms of a species are not identical. Those best suited to the environment survive or fail to survive in terms of the adaptation principle. In this way, there may be progressive differentiation of species in terms of distinct characteristics facilitating adaptation.

Organisms can be arranged on the phylogenetic scale (discussed in the preceding paragraph) in terms of anatomical and physiological similarities. Biological science has enjoyed considerable success in extending findings and generalizations from one species to another; the closer the two species in position on the phylogenetic scale, the greater the likelihood of successful generalization. Findings regarding psychological processes may likewise be extrapolated from one species to a maximally similar species. Among mammals, for example, which include rat, cat, dog, monkey, chimpanzee and man, there are obvious structural, physiological, and also psychological similarities (i.e., all perceive, all learn, all behave emotionally, all manifest physiological conditions which drive them to activity). On the basis

49

of such similarity it has been possible to generalize from one species to another. This is the basic rationale for the use of animals in psychological research.

In addition, animals have certain special values in research:

1. SIMPLICITY. If development of the nervous system is taken as the criterion of complexity of evolutionary development, man is the most complex animal. This means that other animals are simpler than man. If it is possible to understand a simpler organism, the likelihood is increased for being able to understand a more complex animal.

2. CONTROL. Animals can be subject to more precise control than man. They can be regulated 24 hours each day and restricted with regard to food, water, temperature, illumination, sleep, learning opportunities, or in other ways. Even the heredity of subjects can be controlled if the researcher knows sufficiently in advance about the precise characteristics required in his subjects. And, animals can be observed most completely through their entire life spans.

3. SOCIAL ACCEPTABILITY. Many researches cannot be conducted with human beings because it would not be socially acceptable to do so. That is, the research may be fraught with dangers, the effects of which might persist beyond the duration of the research. The problems with regard to inducing pathological behavior or producing brain lesions are obvious.

4. ECONOMY. For the most part, laboratory animals are easily acquired and relatively inexpensive to maintain.

5. CONVENIENCE. Animal subjects are readily available for research participation at the discretion of the experimenter.

The experimental method in physiological psychology has a number of distinct advantages over the clinical method—especially when animal subjects are employed. These advantages include the following:

1. SAMPLE ADEQUACY. A sample of satisfactory size can be obtained with organisms selected carefully.

2. STRUCTURALLY NORMAL SUBJECTS. Research investigations may begin with structurally and physiologically normal organisms, rather than pathological organisms.

3. RECORDS OF PRELESION PERFORMANCE. It is possible to get performance scores prior to any tissue damage. These can serve as base line records for comparison with postsurgical performance.

4. CONTROL GROUPS. Adequate control groups can typically be obtained.

5. CAREFUL PREPARATION FOR OBSERVATION AND MEASUREMENT. Relevant stimulation can be regulated carefully by means of appropriate confinement of organisms and by using appropriately calibrated and automated equipment. The experimental investigator is prepared to make his observations at a particular time and place employing instruments as required to make the most precise measurements.

6. PRECISION OF LESION LOCUS AND MAGNITUDE. Lesions can be made precisely in a variety of ways.

7. LESION VERIFICATION. Experimental organisms subjected to brain damage can be sacrified to verify the characteristics of the lesion as required.

Psychologists ordinarily are concerned with human performance. While it is perfectly legitimate to be interested in animal performance for its own sake, psychologists in general are primarily interested in the meaning of such findings for human attributes. One of the major problems of experimentation with animals is the problem of extrapolation of research findings to the human. As in anatomy and physiology, it is permissible to extrapolate findings from one species to another to the extent that similarities exist between the two species: to the extent that differences exist between the two species, generalizations must be vigilantly qualified.

Experimental Methods in Physiological Psychology. Five major general methods in physiological psychology may be distinguished plus a sixth general miscellaneous category which is included to permit consideration of a variety of specific research instruments.

A. DIRECT SURGICAL PROCEDURES. Direct surgical precedures include all extirpation, destruction, lobotomy, and transection of tissue techniques. It is necessary to study the behavior of organisms both before and after surgery. Often results depend on extent and location of the lesion; frequently this cannot be determined while operating. It is necessary to sacrifice subjects in order to verify the magnitude and location of the lesion. Sections of the nervous system are prepared which are stained, and after microscopic examination, maps are constructed of destroyed areas. Among the several techniques concerned with tissue destruction are (1) electrolysis; (2) thermocoagulation; (3) surgical excision; (4) chemical destruction; and (5) suction.

Two major transectional techniques may be distinguished: (1) Spinal cord transection involves severing connection between various levels of the spinal cord and the brain. (2) Decerebration involves severing connections between various levels of the brain stem, i.e., a variety of decerebrate preparations are possible in that the brain stem can be transected at different levels; when the term is not further qualified, it generally refers to severing at the midbrain level.

Ablational and transectional preparations have been developed in order to simplify the organism and thereby to permit study of particular strata of the central nervous system relatively independently of the influences of other strata. Sometimes it is possible to isolate a patch of the cerebral cortex, cutting around and undercutting all connections with surrounding cortical and subcortical structures, while leaving circulation intact.

In recent years, modification of the Horsley-Clarke stereotaxic instrument has been increasingly used. Use of this instrument requires careful and detailed maps of the brain of the species under study. Lack of such maps excludes many species from stereotaxic investigation. However, where the instrument can be used, it provides for the possibility of making precise lesions in brain areas which the researcher cannot directly observe. Postmortem verification, however, is still required.

Another surgical technique involves "split brain" preparations—animals in which connections between the cerebral hemispheres have been severed. In combination with appropriate sectioning of part of the optic system (i.e., sagittal section of the optic chiasm), stimulation from each eye will be routed to the ipsilateral hemisphere only. By means of such preparations investigators may study the extent to which each cerebral hemisphere functions independently or interdependently in the course of learning and retention.

For example, it has been found that (under the conditions described with an appropriate sectioning of the optic system) a split-brain monkey with a blindfold over the left eye can learn to discriminate between a circle and a triangle; when the blindfold is shifted to the right eye the discrimination must again be learned. Apparently, the two hemispheres are in some respects autonomous. Under the conditions described, an animal may be taught distinct habits with each eye; presumably each habit involves only one cerebral hemisphere independently of the other. Under certain conditions, then, the split-brain operates, at least in some respects, like two separate brains.

Brain or spinal cord lesions may result in loss of basic sensory or motor functions, changes in functions (e.g., occurrence of pathological signs), suppression of function, release of function, etc., as well as alteration in more complex psychological processes such as learning, reasoning, and speech behavior. *Recording*

B. ELECTRICAL PROCEDURES. These are techniques of recording electrical activity of the nervous system. Electroencephalography, action potential technique, and microelectrode technique are the most common.

1. The electroencephalograph requires at least two electrodes fastened to the scalp; the output is amplified and recorded. As earlier discussed, the EEG is recorded from the intact organism.

2. The action potential technique, essentially a refinement of the EEG, requires an electrode on the area of interest and a second electrode on a neutral position of the body. The first or active electrode picks up potential change in the region. The wave recorded is usually complex. The technique may be useful in nervous system mapping. For example, if electrodes are placed on the cerebral cortex and different tones are sounded, by ascertaining which electrode placements disclose electrical activity in response to tones, evidence concerning the limits of the auditory cortex may be acquired. A kind of cortical mapping can be accomplished in this way. Electroencephalographic and action potential techniques are sometimes used to check each other. These techniques may disclose areas and pathways which escape detection by anatomical methods.

3. Microelectrode technique is probably the most refined method of electrical recording. The microelectrode is drawn out so finely that its tip is not much larger than the area of a single cell body. When inserted into the nervous system it enables the researcher to record spike potentials from a small population of neurons and possibly from individual neurons. By such techniques it is possible to study minute areas of the nervous system and to determine which neurons respond to particular kinds of stimulation. *Stim*

C. LOCAL STIMULATION PROCEDURES. Electrical stimulation technique involves the use of a stimulating electrode which may be applied to points on the brain surface. It was by means of this method that the motor areas were first mapped by Fritsch and Hitzig. Also fine wire electrodes may be inserted through the skull and implanted deep in the brain in order to stimulate specific subsurface regions. The animal is free to move about with the implanted electrode and by means of connecting a stimulator to the socket outside the skull, when desired, the researcher can stimulate the area at the tip of the electrode; or he can even arrange an apparatus, such as a bar-pressing chamber, to permit the animal to stimulate itself. By implanting a tiny pipette instead of the electrode, the researcher can direct minute quantities of chemicals in solution to specific brain areas and observe responses. Although other kinds of energy may be used to accomplish local stimulation, electrical and chemical forms are most common.

D. HORMONAL AND BIOCHEMICAL PROCEDURES. A variety of techniques are employed in assessing the effects of hormones and chemical substances on behavior. One technique of ascertaining functions of an endocrine gland involves surgical removal of the gland. Presurgical and postsurgical activity measures, both physiological and behavioral, provide the basis for inferring glandular function. Replacement therapy involves "artificial" replacement, usually via injection, of the hormone (s) of the gland removed. These techniques have a special value where a gland secretes several hormones in that the effects each hormone may be independently evaluated.

In recent years certain drugs such as lysergic acid diethyla-mide (LSD) and mescaline have been observed to produce psychotic-like processes. When administered for purposes of systematically studying psychotic-like thinking and behavior, such induced conditions are called "model psychoses," and the discovery of other drugs and procedures for ameliorating such psychotomimetic states may be attempted; this kind of research may have both theoretical and practical value. Where the psychotomimetic drugs act, why they act, and how they act are important problems which seem certain to attract the attention of research physiological psychologists in the immediate future.

Recently, also, behavioral methods have been increasingly employed to assess the effects of drugs, especially the tranquil-izers and energizers. One of the more popular of these drug assay methods uses the Skinner-box, a chamber containing a metal bar which when pressed releases a pellet of food or other reward to the animal. After animals under specifiable conditions reach a stable level of performance, the effect of a drug may be ascertained by noting its influence in accelerating or depressing rate of bar-pressing activity or otherwise changing the pattern of performance. The device is objective and automatic and appears to be a rather sensitive indicator of biochemical effects on behavior.

E. DEVELOPMENTAL PROCEDURES. The developmental procedures include techniques for correlating indices of anatomical and physiological development of organisms on the one hand, with indices of behavioral development on the other. These procedures are used particularly, although certainly not exclusively, with organisms during prenatal and early postnatal stages. More specifically, many of the techniques may be grouped as follows:

1. Gross intrauterine behavior of the fetus. Gross intrauterine behavior of the fetus can be studied by observation of the maternal abdomen fluoroscopically, by stethoscope, by palpation, or by recording tambours.

2. More refined indications of intrauterine behavior. Special techniques may be instituted to elicit more refined indications of intrauterine reactions: for example, fetal electrocardiograms or fetal electroencephalograms may be obtained.

3. Observation of the biological development and behavioral development of the prematurely born. Occasionally it is necessary that pregnancy be terminated by abortion or Caesarian section before the infant has reached a maturational level which permits survival. With the placental membrane and amniotic sac intact, such fetuses are immediately placed in an appropriate physiological saline solution where they may be studied.

The above include the major techniques by means of which data and principles regarding human psychophysiological development during early life should have been obtained.

With animals, normal behavior and normal biological development may be observed and charted at various developmental levels; organisms are then sacrificed to determine features of structural development. The endeavor is made to correlate these two provinces of development—the behavioral and the biological.

F. GENERAL PHYSIOLOGICAL PROCEDURES. The general physiological procedures are a heterogeneous collection of techniques capable of yielding information about physiological activity. Used in conjunction with techniques which provide information about stimulus situations or behavior, they can provide data of interest to the physiological psychologist.

1. Extraneural Electrical Recording

a. The PSYCHOGALVANOMETER is a device consisting of a recording electrode, lead wires from it to an amplifying apparatus and a kymograph which records changes in the resistance of the skin to the passage of an electric charge. Usually, it is convenient to attach the electrode to the palmar surface of the hand. Ordinarily the skin is resistant to the passage of an electric charge; under certain conditions, however, skin resistance falls. The responses recorded are variously called psychogalvanic response (PGR), galvanic skin response (GSR), and the electrodermal response (EDR).

b. The ELECTROMYOGRAPH is a device consisting of either a surface electrode or a needle electrode which is inserted into muscle to provide indices of action potential of muscle.

c. The ELECTROCARDIOGRAPH (EKG) consists of recording electrodes, an amplifying device, and a recording apparatus which provides information concerning electrical activity of the heart.

2. Cardiovascular Activity

a. The SPHYGMOGRAPH consists of a disk attached to the wrist, lead wires, an amplifying apparatus, and a recorder which graphically indicates pulse rate.

b. The SPHYGMOMANOMETER is a device for recording blood pressure. It consists of an air-tight sleeve which is inflated by an appended pump after being wrapped around the upper arm. The sleeve leads by means of a rubber tube to a mercury-containing U-shaped container, generally of glass, one appendage of which is graduated; deflections in the column of mercury disclose variations in blood pressure.

c. The PLETHYSMOGRAPH is a closed system consisting of a chamber filled with water and a tube leading from this chamber to a recording device. With it, the volume of an organ or member may be measured; since changes in volume are primarily a function of blood flow, the plethysmograph essentially assesses activity of the circulatory system—vasoconstriction and vasodilation—in the organ.

3. Gastrointestinal Actvity

a. The BALLOON TECHNIQUE involves the subject's swallowing a tiny rubber balloon which is connected to a thin tube which in turn communicates with a recording device. Contractions of the stomach modify pressure within the balloon which is mediated through the tube to deflect the pen of a recorder.

b. FLUOROSCOPIC TECHNIQUE involves the subject's consuming a meal or liquid containing a substance which will occlude x-rays. X-rays passing through the subject will project a shadow of the gastrointestinal tract on a fluorescent screen of calcium tungstate.

4. Endocrine Gland Activity

a. Basal metabolism refers to the heat production of an individual at his lowest level of cell chemistry in the waking state. The BASAL METABOLIC RATE (BMR) may be measured directly with the subject occupying a small chamber called a calorimeter. BMR may be measured more indirectly by having the subject recline and rest several hours after his last meal in a room at a temperature of $20°$ C, and under those conditions record oxygen consumption and carbon dioxide production. The volume of oxygen consumed within a given time would yield an index of the quantity of heat produced. Since metabolic rate is largely a function of thyroid gland secretion, the BMR is frequently used as an index of thyroid activity.

5. Other Physiological Indicators

a. The PNEUMOGRAPH is an air-tight pneumatic system consisting of a hollow rubber chamber stretched and fastened around the chest which communicates changes of pressure via a rubber tube to a recording tambour. Respiratory movements initiate pressure variations within the pneumatic system which are conveyed to the recording system. Rate, depth, regularity and pattern of respiration may then be determined. The respiratory cycle consists of two phases—inspiration and expiration. In dealing with the temporal aspects of respiration, the relative duration of each phase may be expressed by the inspiration-expiration ratio, the I/E ratio.

b. URINALYSIS and blood analysis may provide cues concerning the functioning of various systems of the body.

The POLYGRAPH is a series of instruments such as those recently mentioned, which simultaneously makes records of physiological changes. It is especially useful not only from the standpoint of permitting comparisons in relative magnitude of variation in several implicit processes, but also for the observation of *patterns* or *constellations* of change either in response to various stimulating situations or as accompaniments of more overt behavior.

Obviously all techniques utilized in physiological psychology are not well accommodated in the classification system proposed. For example, occasionally biological development is deliberately altered in order to note such effects on the development of psychological processes. To accomplish this end, surgical transplantations or rearrangements of tissue are sometimes attempted with experimental animals. Receptor structures, effector structures, and nervous tissue are most generally involved in surgical transplantation techniques. Limbs have been transplanted from one part of an organism to another or even from organism to organism of a species; and among salamanders the eye may be rotated in its socket after severing the optic nerve. These kinds of researches might be classified under developmental procedures, but perhaps they could equally well be classified with surgical procedures. Since they are both, the techniques do not fit exclusively into either category. However, the classification proposed does appear to accommodate a large variety of the major techniques now being utilized to further knowledge in the area of physiological psychology.

Summary Statement on Methods of Physiological Psychology

In recent years there have been expansions in the horizons of physiological psychology and a concomitant development in its methodology. For example, observations and measurements of many types are being made within the brain substance of normal unanesthetized animals; and mechanisms deep within the brain are also being rather directly manipulated by research investigators. As a consequence of these and other accomplishments, vast quantities of new data are being acquired; with analysis of these data revolutionary new concepts are evolving and there are indications of meaningful progress in understanding brain mechanisms which are of special significance to the psychologist.

Perhaps it would not be inappropriate to state briefly at this point a few general principles relating to methodology in physiological psychology:

1. Each method and technique has its own advantages and each has its limitations.

2. A more complete perspective of a given area is obtained by using a variety of techniques; each technique provides but a single physiological aspect of a complex process. Furthermore experimental research results should accord with clinical research results; results of research with animals and humans should disclose meaningful correspondences. Or at least discrepancies should be explicable.

3. There are formidable intricacies in the nervous system and the rest of the physiological matrix which underlies behavior. Objective instruments and techniques of increasing sensitivity and precision have been devised in recent years and a variety of new behavioral methods have been developed. The increased scope of the field and the innovations and improvements in techniques for observation, data acquisition, and data analysis, promise to revolutionize conceptualizations of brain functioning in general and behavioral mechanisms in particular. More precise information about relationships between anatomical and physiological variables on the one hand and behavior on the other will emerge with further development and improvement in techniques, procedures, and methods. The promise is bright if fruitful gains of recent years can be sustained and continued.

References

Comprehensive surveys of methods in physiological psychology have been infrequent, although there are a number of papers which discuss relatively discrete techniques and procedures. Further information on methods of physiological psychology is obtainable from several different chapters in Osgood's book and in the handbook edited by Stevens both of which are listed below. Informa-

tion about more recent developments, however, must be obtained
from the journal literature.

Lindsley, D. B. Studying neuropsychology and bodily functions.
   In T. G. Andrews (Ed.) *Methods of psychology*. New York:
   John Wiley & Sons, 1948.
Osgood, C. E. *Method and theory in experimental psychology*.
   New York: Oxford University Press, 1953.
Stevens, S. S. (Ed.) *Handbook of experimental psychology*. New
   York: John Wiley & Sons, 1951.

INDEX

INDEX

INDEX

Magendie, Francois (1783-1855), 12, 17
Manometer, 38
Mechanistic notion, 6-7, 21
Mechanists, French, 8-9
Medulla, 13, 37
Meninges, 37, 38
Meprobamate, 27, 41
Mescaline, 27, 54
Methods, 29-59
  basic biological, 30-32
  clinical, 30, 32-49
  experimental, 30, 49-58
  special diagnostic, 36-41
  special therapeutic, 41-43
Mettrie, Julien Offroy de la (1709-1751), 9
Microscopic observation, 31-32
Microelectrode technique, 43
Midbrain, 27
Milieu interne, 17
Miltown, 27
Mind, 6-8
Mind-Body Problem, 5-8
  animism, 5
  Aristotle's view of, 6
  Descartes view of, 6
  double aspect theory, 6
  dualism, philosophical, 6
  Leibnitz's view of, 7
  psychophysical interactionism, 6
  psychophysical parallelism, 7
  Spinoza's view of, 7
Mirabeau, 9
Model psychoses, 54
Monistic philosophy, 7
Moniz, Egas, 42
Morgan, C. Lloyd (1852-1936), 19, 21
Motor centers, 18
Motor functioning, 36
Mueller, Johannes P., 13, 14, 15, 20
Murphy, G. 28

Negative feedback. 23
Nerve impulse velocity, 14
Nervous system evolution, doctrine of, 16
Neurological examination, 34-36
Neurology of learning, 26
Neurosurgical effects, 33
Nicotine, 7

Observation, gross, 31
  microscopic, 31-32
Olds, James, 26
Ophthalmoscope, 41
Ophthalmoscopy, 36, 41
Optic disk, 41
Organic brain disorder, 32-33
  acute, 32
  chronic, 33
Osgood, C. E., 60

Pantheism, 7
Pavlov, Ivan P. (1849-1936), 20
Phase sequence, 26

Phenomenon, rebound, 36
Philosophical dualism, 6
Phrenology, 5, 10-12, 28
  attacks on, 10-11
  value of, 11
Phylogenetic scale, 49
Physics, 28
Physiognomy, 4-5
Physiological gradient, 22
Physiological psychology
  definition of, 3
  basic objective of, 3
  province of, 4
  recent contributions to, 23-26
Pia mater, 37
Pineal gland, 7
Pituitary gland, 25
Pituitary gland, 25
Plato, 8
Plethysmograph, 56
Pneumoencephalography, 36, 39, 48
Pneumograph, 57
Polygraph, 58
Pons, 37
Positive feedback, 23-24
Procedures for studying
  accidental destruction of tissue, 33
  effects of neurosurgery, 34
  pathological changes, 33-34
Pseudopsychophysiologies, 4-5
Psychogalvanometer, 56
Psychopharmacology, 25-26
Psychophysical interactionism, 6
Psychophysical parallelism, 7
Psychophysiology of learning, 23
Psychosis, lead, 44
Psychoses, model, 54
Psychosurgery, 34, 42
Psychotomimetic drugs, 26, 27, 54
Punishment center 25-26
Pupil, Argyll-Robertson, 44
Pythagoras, 8

Radiation, ultrasonic, 43
Rauwolfia serpentina, 27
Reaction, alarm, 25
  conditioned, 20
  emergency, 21
  stress, 24-25
Rebound phenomenon, 36
Reflex, 13, 20
Replacement therapy, 54
Reserpine, 27, 41
Resistance stage, 25
Response, 3
  Babinski, 36
Reticular activating system, ascending, 41
Retina, 41
Reward center, 25-26
Romberg sign, 36
Roots, law of the, 12

Sechenov, Ivan M. (1829-1905), 20
Selye, Hans, 24-25
Septal area, 26

63

INDEX